FOUR SEASONS ON A
WESTMORLAND FARM

FOUR SEASONS ON A WESTMORLAND FARM

Andrea Meanwell

HAYLOFT PUBLISHING LTD

Published by Hayloft Publishing Ltd., 2019

A CIP catalogue record for this book is available from the British Library

ISBN 978-1-910237-57-1

Hayloft policy is to use papers that are natural, renewable and recyclable
products and made from wood grown in sustainable forests. The logging
and manufacturing processes are expected to conform to the
environmental regulations of the country of origin.

Designed, printed and bound in the EU

Hayloft Publishing Ltd,
a company registered in England number 4802586
2 Staveley Mill Yard, Staveley, Kendal, LA8 9LR (registered office)
L'Ancien Presbytère, 21460 Corsaint, France (editorial office)

Email: books@hayloft.eu
Tel: 07971 352473
www.hayloft.eu

For the residents of Low Borrowbridge Farm
Past, present and future

FOUR SEASONS ON A WESTMORLAND FARM

Contents

*Low Burrowbridge on Jefferys map of
Westmorland, 1770.*

Prologue

The sun rose while they were crossing the moor, a dazzle of light over the tops of the hills. The sunshine crept down the slopes into the peaceful green valleys, where the white cottages nestled in gardens and orchards 'That's Westmorland,' said Pig Wig

The Tale of Pigling Bland
Beatrix Potter

The day after we bought the farm I took my mum and dad in the car, and drove them down the Fairmile Road. Three and a half miles after we set off from the farmhouse we stopped and got out, looking down Lunesdale.

"That's the end of the farm there, in those woods. So it's all the land from the farmhouse to here, between the River Lune and the railway line."

"It's massive" said Dad. "It goes on for miles. It's actually a proper big farm."

"I know" I said, "that's what we wanted. A proper big farm."

In early December 1976 I was standing at the window in our 'front room' in York. I had recently learned to write, and am helping my mum address Christmas card envelopes. She has written the addresses of my family onto pieces of paper and I am copying them onto the envelopes.

I can just about fit WESTMORLAND onto the envelope. It is such a long, lyrical word. I look at the word, and I look out of the window. I imagine where this card is going. I know Westmorland; it means a land of sheep, cows, hens, dogs and trains. The ancient names of the county are just as poetic: Westmereland or Westmoringland.

In reality, Westmorland ceased to exist in 1974, but stoically we refuse to give up on the county and write it boldly onto the envelopes. Westmorland, an elusive place, had cast a spell on me.

School and University

The year is now 1986 and I am sitting in the careers room at my large comprehensive school in York, filling out a multiple choice tick sheet about what I would like to do with my life. The sheets are collected by the teachers, and the following week we will receive the opinion of the computer that has been 'scientifically programmed' with all the possible career alternatives available to us. We do not get to see the computer, as the school does not, to my knowledge, have a single computer on the premises. Typing and engineering drawing are still curriculum subjects, and it is impossible for us to imagine that soon these skills will be out-dated by the advent of the computer.

The following week I received a slip of paper with my career options:

- Animal laboratory technician
- Primary school teacher
- Secondary school teacher

I was absolutely horrified with option 1. The animals I have encountered so far in my life have been my dog, and my uncle's flock of free ranging Swaledale sheep. The idea of working with animals in a laboratory appalled me.

Having done well at school there was a general opinion that I should go to university, and not just any old university, a 'Russell group' university to study a 'proper academic subject'. Going to a teacher training college did not

11

seem to be an option, the teachers at school being very disparaging of teaching as a career and were reassuring me that I could always do a postgraduate course in teaching if I wanted to.

My parents were very encouraging about this plan, as a career in teaching was seen as a very secure option, particularly as it had such a good pension scheme. Pension schemes were not something that I concerned myself with considering, but I agreed to follow the plan of going to university. After all, it was free to study and I would get a maintenance grant for my living expenses. There was no good reason not to go.

I flicked through some university prospectuses in the careers room. The room was in a 1960s building and had a wall of glass, so it was like sitting in a greenhouse. Nobody wanted to spend any time in there looking at their career options; it was too hot and airless. The prospectus I picked up first was for Manchester University, although it's not its academic prowess that interests me, but the music scene there that I had been reading about each week in the *New Musical Express*. There were two 'academic' subjects that seemed practical. I am a very practical, doing person and wanted to study something that involved being outside.

The first subject was landscape architecture. I didn't really know what landscape architecture was, but you required an A Level in art to study it that I didn't have, so that was out. The second subject was archaeology. I had the correct A Level subjects to apply for this, so archaeology it was.

I attended an interview at Manchester, where memorably one of the questions was "Why would Elizabeth I have said, "I am Richard" on watching the play Richard II?" I am offered a ridiculously low offer to study there, as I am able to waffle on for ages answering this question in great detail.

Meanwhile the City of York, where we were living, was buzzing with archaeological activity. There was a rescue dig on the site of the Stakis Hotel, and the dig had been on every news bulletin for its exciting finds; a major public building, possibly a bath complex, had been uncovered. The walls of the building survived up to 3.5m high and are 2.2m thick. There were tile-lined openings in the wall, and the drains had also survived.

The head of my Sixth Form called me into her office and said that as the dig was of national importance, and as I was about to embark upon a career as an archaeologist, I could have two weeks off school to go and work on the dig.

So the following Monday morning I cycled with my packed lunch not to school, but to the archaeological dig and offered my services. As I had no experience of excavation I was told I could work voluntarily in the finds department for two weeks. Looking back now it seems remarkable that I could just turn up on a Monday morning with no prior contact with the archaeological trust, or references from school, and start work on site immediately, but that's how it was.

The finds department was a Portakabin on site, into which the archaeologists brought finds caked in mud. I had to clean the finds and then categorize each find and label it with the location that it had been found. Somebody taught me the types of finds on the first morning, and then I was basically left alone to work in the Portakabin for two weeks cleaning and categorizing Medieval sheep's teeth and large quantities of Roman building materials.

After these two weeks were up there was then another rescue dig where there was a development on Micklegate in York. There was a very limited amount of time to excavate the site before the builders moved in and it was all hands to the pump. The head of Sixth Form had again seen this on the news, and when I returned to school on the Monday morning after the Stakis dig she told me to go and work on the Micklegate dig as it would be a 'once in a lifetime opportunity'.

The weather during the two weeks I was on the dig was appalling. The archaeologist in charge asked what experience I had, "Finds at Stakis", and set me to work on the finds there. There were two of us armed with toothbrushes and a hosepipe of cold water, sat on the side of one of the trenches in the rain. The archaeologists brought us trays of finds, and we cleaned them and catalogued them. Our hands were like ice from working outside with the cold hosepipe, and there was no comfy Portakabin to retreat from the rain into. It was difficult to write the labels in the rain.

I was very glad when the two weeks ended, without finding anything of significance, and I could go back to school. I avoided seeing the head of Sixth Form in the corridors in case she had seen any more archaeological digs on the news.

I loved living and working in the City of York. After finishing at the archaeological digs each day I pushed my bike through The Shambles on the way home. This is a narrow street full of half-timbered medieval buildings filled with tiny shops. One of the shop windows always caught my eye as it had an automated 'Shoemaker' in the window making shoes, hitting his hammer onto his tiny workbench. It was an old-fashioned shop where you could still have a last made of your feet and buy homemade, made to measure shoes. In the window during the weeks of the archaeological digs there was a sign in the window saying 'Apprentice shoemaker required. Apply within.' It took me all my willpower to push the bike past the shop window each night and not call in. Going to university was a great opportunity. Nobody in my family had ever been to university before, and I had to make the most of it.

Studying archaeology did not turn out to be the practical course that I had hoped for, but after graduating I managed to get a job in the Yorkshire Museum in York. This was a two-day a week job, manning the museum as part of the skeleton weekend staff. On Monday to Friday I went to St John's College in York to do my postgraduate teaching course, and on Saturday and Sunday I worked in the museum. My vague plan was once I had my teaching qualification and the experience in the museum I could get a job working as an education officer for a heritage charity such as English Heritage on Hadrian's Wall. This would allow me to live and work in Cumbria, working outdoors teaching people about the history of the North of England.

The museum had been built and stocked as a two-storey museum to display the finds and heritage of Yorkshire. There were initially two storeys full of glass cases of archaeological finds from the City of York. The museum had later been refurbished, and was now open to the public only on the ground floor. The ground floor consisted of a temporary exhibition, such as automated dinosaurs, then a permanent exhibition about the Romans, Vikings and later settlers in Northern England.

There were four of us manning the museum at weekends and we took turns to man the entrance, Roman gallery, 'jewel' and 'free'. In the entrance we would greet visitors, and look out across the museum gardens for any suspicious activity. In the Roman gallery we would wander through the gallery and answer any questions that the public had.

The 'jewel' was the Middleham Jewel. The museum had recently acquired the jewel for 2.5 million pounds. It had been found by a metal detector, and reputably held the finger of a saint inside the locket wrapped in silk. The insurance policy for the jewel stipulated that it had to be guarded at all times during opening hours, as well as being heavily alarmed. One of us had to sit on a high stool next to the jewel and carefully observe the people who came to see it.

Officially we were not allowed to divert our eyes from the jewel, or move off the stool. Unofficially it was actually very hard in the winter, when there were perhaps five to ten visitors per day, to sit still on the stool.

The jewel was protected by an elaborate system of laser alarms, and I would see how near to the jewel I could get without tripping one of the lights on the alarm system. I could never get nearer than 5m in front of the jewel, no matter how hard I tried. If you have seen the animation *The Wrong Trousers* where Grommit is sent to steal a jewel you will be able to imagine what I was doing. I did not, unfortunately, have the ex-NASA techno trousers to walk along the ceiling of the museum, which would have made it more interesting.

The fourth position, 'free', allowed you to wander around the museum, checking on the public and making sure all the visitors were happy. Often in the winter there would be no visitors to check up on, and I would get the key for the deserted upper galleries. I would keep in regular communication with the other staff via walkie talkie who would tell me if any visitors came in and I needed to come back downstairs, but I had an amazing opportunity to handle hundreds of artefacts and educate myself about them. I also memorised all the information on the boards in the Roman galleries during these quiet times, and sometimes sat and read archaeological journals and magazines that were left in the museum office.

By the time I finished my formal education and was a qualified teacher, I was also a mini expert on Roman Britain. Why I was accumulating all this knowledge was unknown, and for a long time I thought that the only good thing to come out of those years in Higher Education was meeting my husband and getting married. I can now see, however, that there was a grand plan. There was a reason that I needed all this knowledge. The reason was that in 2018 I was to become the owner of a Roman fort and civilian settlement, which provides 'an important insight into a wide range of aspects of civilian and military life during the Roman occupation of Britain' (Historic England).

Low Borrowbridge

It was not only physically beautiful, it was a place in which she felt emotionally rooted as a descendant of hard-working north-country folk. The predictable routines of farm life appealed to her. There was a longing... to find a place where time moved slowly.

Linda Lear writing about Beatrix Potter.

Just like the first time that I saw The Syke where we lived for eight years in the Lake District, the first time that I saw our current farm was when we went to a fell race. My husband was running in the Fairmile fell race, part of the Kendal Winter League series, and I had gone along to watch. Before the start, while the runners were warming up, I began exploring. The race was a gut bursting steep climb up and out of the Lune Valley to the top of Fell Head and back down, a little horseshoe.

We parked at the side of the Lune in the Lune Valley just down from the Lune Gorge. I decided to try and walk down to the riverbank through the dead bracken. As I got part way down and looked across the valley I could see a deserted farm on the other side of the river. It looked like there were three houses, a barn, a vegetable garden, and an orchard. There was no road to or from the property. 'How intriguing,' I thought. There were very few deserted farms like this in the Lake District due to the high value placed on Lake District property. It was certainly very unusual in Cumbria to see a deserted farmstead like this. It looked to have been occupied within living memory. What an interesting place.

When the race started I ran to the top of Fell Head and then ran back down to the car. It was certainly an exhilarating, spectacular landscape. So exhilarating that I got carried away with the sheer joy of running fast downhill and tumbled head over heels, pulling a muscle in my neck/shoulder.

Once the decision had been taken that my family would try and move farms, after our attempts at getting a farm tenancy with the National Trust and the Ministry of Defence had been unsuccessful, we began to look at farms that we considered might be affordable. We first looked at Low Borrowbridge on 31 December 2016. At this point we didn't even bother to look inside the farmhouse. It might seem odd to people who do not have animals to consider, but the condition of the farmhouse was the last thing on our mind. We liked the land and farm buildings, as much of it as we could see on our own without keys to get through gates, so we made an appointment with the agent to view.

I also mentioned it to my parents who had a drive out to look at the farm for themselves. They were met in the farmyard by someone who was looking round, who told them in no uncertain terms that he would be buying the farm, so there was no point in them looking. We then knew there were other people interested in buying the farm, and we would have to decide if we wanted to attempt to buy it reasonably quickly.

The farm had been a very large farm, reputedly the

largest farm in the old county of Westmorland before the county boundaries were changed in the 1970s. It had been farmed by the Wilson family, along with a neighbouring farm at High Carlingill, since 1965. Once they had decided to sell the farm, after selling High Carlingill, it was split into seven lots:

Lot 1 comprised of the farmhouse and associated buildings, traditional hay barns with stables under, old milking parlour, modern farm buildings and 31 acres of meadows around the house, one of which contained a Roman fort. This really grabbed my attention as something very interesting and out of the ordinary.

Lot 2 comprised of almost 20 acres of meadows.

Lot 3 contained the old ruined farm buildings that I had seen from the Fairmile fell race, and the 133 acres surrounding it, previously known as Low Park Farm. This lot had at one time been an independent farm. It had ceased to be a farm with the coming of the M6 motorway, and had been unoccupied since 1967. Its land was now sandwiched between the West Coast Railway line and the River Lune.

Lots 4, 5 and 6 together comprised of 638 acres of moorland and woodland, and Lot 7 was a small paddock of around an acre.

The seven lots had been auctioned in August 2016. Lots 2, 4, 5, 6 and 7 had sold at auction, leaving lots 1 and 3 remaining. This presented the ideal opportunity for us. We could renovate the farmhouse and farm the area around the farmhouse with my rare breed sheep. I could develop a,

diversification business around the Roman Fort/farm walks. Low Park Farm would give our middle son Hector the land he needed to expand his numbers of both sheep and cattle.

It was, therefore, the ideal opportunity for our family. We decided that we would have a go at buying it. Several obstacles had to be overcome, most of them financial. We would have to sell our current house and our two holiday cottages. We would also have to sell our current farmland, by auction, and also possibly borrow money from our family.

None of that (except borrowing money from our family, for which we have to be very grateful to both sets of my grandparents who were so thrifty and hardworking) proved to be straightforward. So it was with great relief that in February 2018 I met John Wilson at the farmhouse and he handed me his keys, along with the shepherds guide to show the sheep mark that we had inherited, and the horn burning irons for marking sheep from Low Borrowbridge. There was even doubt on the day of moving about whether he would be able to move his sheep off because snow was forecast, but it worked out as planned.

Hector was going to move into the farmhouse straight away, with the rest of the family following on later. I left the key under a piece of wood next to the back door, and when Hector returned home from working at a neighbouring farm he became the first Meanwell to move into Low Borrowbridge farm, the first new farmer to take over the farm for 53 years.

The Farm

Resources at 30th March 2018:

Farmhouse, built partly in 16th, 17th and 18th centuries.

Old bar and tap room (had been used as a Sunday School)

Derelict farmhouse and three derelict barns.

Range of traditional barns including cow shippons with haybarn over, stabling for three horses, hired lads room, hay mew, turnip stores and pigsties.

Milking parlour built in 1947.

Range of modern agricultural buildings including cow shed and lambing shed.

Silage pit and slurry store.

54 Rough Fell ewes and gimmer hoggs

18 Ouessant ewes and gimmer hoggs

24 Herdwick ewes

11 Welsh Hill Speckle Faced ewes and gimmer hoggs

10 Shetland/Ryeland ewes

Welsh tup, Ryeland tup and Ouessant tup.

6 Dexter cows

3 Fell ponies

2 Hens

6 Border collies

A Lakeland terrier and a Lancashire heeler

164 acres grazing and mowing land

16 year old Land Rover

Small sheep trailer and large livestock trailer

One old International tractor and one old Ford tractor, bale spike and bucket

One woman, two sons (another at university) and a woring husband.

February and March 2018

Bad weather in itself means little to the sheep on high.
But there is one danger. Should heavy snow be succeeded
by continuous hard frost, all grazing becomes imprisoned
under this concrete covering. Then, even the Herdwick
and Swaledale are almost helpless.
Thinking of the freezing, wind-torn night, it was hard to
believe that any creature of flesh and blood could have
remained alive up here.

Under Scafell, Dudley Hoys (1955)

The first time we viewed inside the house Hilary Wilson, sister-in-law of Michael Wilson who had lived there, warned us before we went into the house that her brother-in-law had lived in the house for many years 'bachelor style'. I had been slightly prepared for what we were about to see as I had searched for #lowborrowbridgefarm on Instagram and had seen a set of photographs of the interiors by a photographer. These photographs included a pink bath, a Victorian pram, an old tweed coat hung on a peg and various shots of 1960s wallpaper.

The house is a traditional Westmorland (Westmorland was a historic county before it was abolished in 1974 and amalgamated into the new county of Cumbria) farmhouse. It has been expanded over the years. Hilary also commented that it was remarkable that the Romans had central heating in their fort on the site 2,000 years ago, but the house had never had central heating.

There was a large farm kitchen, three lounges, an old kitchen complete with flag floor and range, walk in pantry, two bathrooms (one with a huge Victorian bath no longer plumbed in) and six bedrooms. Some of these rooms were in the barns at the back of the house, and there was potential to go further into the barns to expand more. There were also various domestic outbuildings, and a long low building which had served many purposes over the years including a Sunday school and a navvies tavern for the builders of the Lancaster to Carlisle railway between 1844 and 1846.

On an initial look round it seemed to me that the house could easily be split into three smaller properties. This would require quite a lot of work (two kitchens and one extra bathroom for starters) and wasn't something we could afford to do straight away whilst we were still selling our other properties and farmland. We decided to temporarily decorate a small area of the house that we could live in while we decided exactly what to do.

I decided to decorate three bedrooms and two lounges. On the first room that I took the wallpaper off it became apparent that I would need the help of a plasterer, and work was put on hold for a while. I managed to find a local plasterer who said he would be able to come and plaster the wall, and I decided that I had better take up the bedroom carpet. Underneath the carpet was an envelope addressed to 'Mrs J Wilson'. It was sealed up.

By chance John Wilson came by later that day, and I passed him the envelope. He said that was his mother's name, and opened the envelope and looked inside. I hoped that it wasn't a letter that she was hiding from her family, but it was actually one hundred pounds in very old bank notes. What a find, and poor Mrs Wilson leaving it there undiscovered. It must have been quite a large sum of money at the time of hiding.

"Keep on looking," said John, "you never know what else you will find." Whilst these renovations were taking place Hector lived in one of the bedrooms, heated by a plug in radiator. It was a long, cold winter with temperatures regularly falling below zero.

We moved the sheep, ponies and cows over to Low Borrowbridge at weekends. At the time of moving we had six Dexter cows, three Fell ponies and around 150 sheep. There was my flock of 20 Ouessant sheep (the world's smallest breed of sheep), ten Ryeland/Shetland ewes that were in lamb to a Ryeland (my fibre producing sheep), sixteen Welsh Hill Speckle Faced sheep, 25 Herdwick sheep (recently bought from a fell farm in the Lake District by Hector, in lamb to a Beltex/Charolais tup) and our flock of Rough Fell sheep. Rough Fells and Herdwicks are both breeds native to Cumbria, and the Welsh Speckles had come from a similar upland environment in Snowdonia.

We had bought a large trailer to move the animals. Our sheep had only ever been in a small trailer before and were very reluctant to go up the ramp onto the top deck, as the ramp was much steeper than anything that they had ever experienced before. I felt sorry for them standing there looking at the ramp, trying to work it out. Eventually we had to carry one sheep up the ramp and pop her into the top deck to show them what we wanted them to do.

The cows were trickier to transport, as a new calf did

not want to come into the holding area that we load them from. The older cows were very happy to come into the holding area and get into the trailer, as they know that they will be going to fresh grass, but the little calf was not so sure. It took us three separate attempts on three separate days to get him to come in.

The ponies were keen to put on their leads and walk over to the trailer as they had been conservation grazing a

Looking down over 'Lot 3' from the Howgill Fells.

large area of rush and were no doubt impatient to get to a new field. Susan and Bella shot up the ramp into the trailer, but Apple would not put her feet onto the ramp. I kept saying that she just needed time, but after an hour of saying this the other ponies began to get impatient on the trailer, so I had to physically put her feet onto the ramp and push her bottom up into the trailer.

It was now the end of February and very cold. Snow was forecast for the week that we moved the cows so we put them into one of the barns. The news was full of the weather forecast, the worst snow for ten years was predicted in some areas as the 'Beast from the East', an easterly wind, was coming blowing snow from Russia. The forecast didn't look too bad for Tebay, and as we met in a local pub for a friend's 50th birthday the weekend before the forecast snow a friend said, "I don't think it will trouble us."

Our younger sheep, the hoggs that were not in lamb, and our tups were put into small fields around the farmhouse, but the older sheep were allowed to wander along the River Lune down towards Low Park Farm, a distance of about two and a half miles. They all settled happily, and showed no interest in coming over for food as there was plenty of grass to eat. As they were not hanging around in a big gang, waiting for food, they spread out much more than they would have normally done.

The plan was that we would keep an eye on them by driving the length of the farm on the track there, but basically they were 'turned away', happy 'at grass'. We met some of our new neighbours. Everybody was talking about the expected snow, but saying that if it did snow it would be gone by 10am.

Hector had organised a big transporter to come and move all our farming equipment. We had piled it up at the side of our old house, and there was a surprisingly large accumulation of hayracks, hurdles, buckets and all manner of things in addition to his tractor. The transporter could not park in front of the house, as it would block the road, so it reversed down a tiny lane at the side of the house and parked. This lane gave access to two properties, and there was another lane to get in/out should anyone need to get to one of the houses.

We had just begun to load the transporter, with our entire family helping and one of Hector's friends, when a convoy of 4x4 vehicles appeared at the top of the road and started driving down towards the transporter. "I'm sorry," I said, "we are just moving farms, you will have to reverse back up the lane and go out the other way."

"Reverse?" said the driver. "We are learning how to drive off-road, we can't reverse, we haven't been taught how to. You will have to move the truck."

"It's really easy to reverse a Land Rover," I said. "I'll do it for you if you don't want to?"

"Oh no," said the driver "I can't let you do that because it is not our Land Rover. We can't reverse so you will have to move the truck."

Generally I would say I am quite a calm person, but it must have been the stress of moving house.

"Honestly! If you can't reverse a Land Rover you should not be driving it." I stormed off to tell the driver that he would have to move the truck due to the driver's inability to reverse. My Land Rover was parked in front of his truck.

"Hang on" I said, "I'll just move my Land Rover first." I jumped into the Land Rover, and as if to demonstrate how easy it was to reverse a Land Rover I reversed around the corner in front of the house… and straight into the back of Hector's friend's car. That will teach me for losing my temper. Any money saved in ordering a large transporter and moving the equipment in one go rather than in separate trips with our trailer had now been lost in the repair bill for the car.

"Do you know those people couldn't reverse a Land Rover?" I said to everyone helping "Well, neither it seems can I."

We woke on Wednesday, 28 February to about three inches of snow in Rusland. Fergus' school was closed, so we decided to go over to Low Borrowbridge in the Land Rover after we had walked the dogs. Checking online, however, the motorway was closed and the police were telling people not to attempt to travel. After 1pm the motorway reopened so we set off from home. The journey was windy and snowy, but the snowploughs had cleared a route through the snow. A neighbour had ploughed the lane past our house and we were able to get there relatively easily, although the engine management light kept flashing on the Land Rover as it was about -7 degrees.

When we arrived Hector had got the Ouessant sheep into the yard, and we got them into one of the buildings and bedded them down with straw so that they were out of the weather. There was about a foot of snow in the farmyard, but where it had drifted it was about waist deep. It was too deep for the tiny Ouessants to be outside.

Hector had fed some of the sheep close to home, who

seemed fine, and he set off in his tractor to drive the length of the track to feed the older sheep. What he hadn't expected was the depth of some of the snowdrifts. The track is quite undulating, and he couldn't get through some of the drifts uphill, which he estimated were about six feet deep. He tried to go up the track forwards and backwards, but couldn't get through the snow. The tractor was stuck fast, he had to leave it and continue on foot. He then carried some silage for about a mile to the sheep in that area, but couldn't physically get through the snow for the last mile and a half.

He phoned me and we agreed that we would leave the sheep for another day and I would walk down tomorrow. The forecast for the next day was much better. Sheep, particularly older ones that have lived on the fells are usually very good at finding shelter and keeping themselves safe. It can sometimes do more harm than good to call them out of their sheltered hiding places for food. Our only concern was that the sheep did not know this land. They would not know the safe places to hide. They may choose to shelter where the snow blew in drifts.

In Rusland I had known someone who had lost 300 sheep in a storm like this. They had gone into a hollow to shelter, and a lot of snow had blown over them. The snow had then frozen on the surface over the top of them and formed a hard crust. They had then struggled to breathe and had suffocated. We would have to hope for the best, there was nothing else we could do as night fell.

Back in the farmyard both Hector's car and tractor had frozen solid. There were icicles hanging from the car and from the drainpipes of the house. The outlets from the sinks had frozen up. We would have to hope that tomorrow brought a better day. I didn't get much sleep that night wondering about where the sheep were and if they were safe.

Hector had managed to defrost his car and charge the battery and had set off to work when I got back to the farm the following morning. He had already fed all the sheep close to home before he left, but I decided to check them again. Going across the farmyard was difficult. The snow had set solid in thigh deep ridges so that it looked like a frozen sea with big waves set in ice. Then, with unbelievable ferocity, Storm Emma arrived.

The wind started swirling around the farmyard picking up snow. Where our neighbour had ploughed the land down to the farm the previous day and moved the snow to the sides of the lane, it was whipped up and thrown about landing in random piles metres deep. There was no way that I could attempt to drive down the lane in the Land Rover so I set off on foot to try and get to the sheep. As I reached the banks of the River Lune near the Salterwath Bridge I could see swirling snow coming down the Lune Gorge towards me. It filled the gorge up to the fell tops, and looked like a huge snow tornado coming at me. It was like watching a movie about extreme weather events. I braced myself with my back to the wind, ready to feel the wind, but instead of pushing against me as I expected it picked me up along with the snow and deposited me about five metres further down the track.

I picked myself up off the ground, and looked down the valley again. Another swirl of snow was coming towards me. Instinct took over and I stood facing the wall of swirling snow for about 20 seconds, then as it swirled towards me without thinking I lay down on the track in the snow in a foetal position with my hands over my head. I closed my eyes as it passed over me, and when I opened them it had not picked me up. It was totally disorientating in the swirling snow as it settled.

I could now see the ponies and walked over to them. They seemed fine. Native ponies are bred to survive the elements and they were doing a remarkable job of looking unflustered by the weather, unlike me. All the sheep I could see from the first mile of the track looked fine as well. I would have to trust that I had chosen the right breeds for our environment. Again, it was going to be safer to leave them than attempt to get to them in the storm on foot. The snowdrifts were impassable on foot, and the wind made the situation simply too dangerous to continue alone.

Shell-shocked I walked back to the farmhouse. The environment was certainly challenging us in our first week at Low Borrowbridge. To think that I had imagined that the sheep would peacefully graze along the banks of the River Lune incubating their lambs. It was now an out and out survival situation. Would the flock survive the storm? Would the farmhouse and the barns survive the storm? I know they had been there for hundreds of years, and they must have seen some storms in that time, but I had never seen anything like the snow tornados in my lifetime. It took me all the strength that I had to walk through the snow and wind back home, holding my hat onto my head and my scarf around my face, life was certainly going to be challenging here.

Hector didn't make it back to Low Borrowbridge that night. It had taken him four hours to dig a route up to the farm where he was working that day, and he had spent the rest of the daylight hours digging sheep out of the snow. The flock of about 250 sheep had retreated to an old farmhouse and had got snowed in there. The doorways had filled with snow, and they took some digging out. He had then slept there, exhausted.

The next morning he drove back to Low Borrowbridge followed by his friend in a Land Rover in case he got stuck. They managed to get to the lane end and then walk to the farm. He set off to look for the sheep saying, "Nothing's impossible" when I said it was impossible to get to them. We hadn't seen the sheep at this point for three days, three days of snow and wind. Today was earmarked as our official 'moving day' and we were due to move our furniture and possessions to Low Borrowbridge, but there was no point in even driving to the car hire company to pick up the van we had rented to move, as there was no way that we would get the van down the road to the farm through the snow.

I busied myself doing animal jobs around the farm while he searched for them. There was a lot of work to be done fetching and carrying water as all the water troughs and outside water taps were frozen solid. I feared the worst for the sheep, and was sure that there would be casualties. I blamed myself for not taking enough heed of the weather forecasts, and had to keep reminding myself that it was Yorkshire that was forecast for the snow and not our area. Should we have moved the sheep? Had we sent them off unknowingly to certain death in the snow?

Phones kept shutting down when you took them out of pockets because of the extreme cold, but after about an

Winter struggle to feed stock.

hour I got a snatched phone call with Hector who said that several large trees were down, and some sheep were dead underneath an oak tree. He was making good progress, although he was saying "I've made a mistake coming this way…" when his phone shut down and the call ended abruptly.

Half an hour later there was another quick phone call to say that he had been walking through a snowdrift when he looked down and saw just a tongue sticking out from the snow. He dug down and found one of his Herdwicks. It looked like she had been eating her own fleece. He pulled her out and then she was off – what a remarkable breed the Herdwick is. Our Herdwicks had come from the fells near Broughton In Furness and would be very hardy, surviving

35

at high altitudes in all weathers without human intervention for the majority of the year. The phone shut down again, but now I had real hope that he would find and save the sheep.

I continued working in the farmyard. The doors of the lambing shed had been blown off during the night and the buildings were making a lot of bangs and rattles in the wind, but everything else seemed to be safe. It wasn't only me that had been picked up by the wind as some of the large hayracks on wheels were now in different fields to the ones they had been previously, with lids blown off and wheels smashed off.

Then I got the phone call that I had been waiting for, Hector was now down in the buildings at Low Park Farm, along with all of the missing sheep. They had all gone into the derelict farm buildings, and thankfully snow had not blocked the doors. All of the remaining sheep were accounted for and Hector was on his way back. I put the kettle on the Rayburn and breathed a huge sigh of relief. Such sensible sheep, and such a determined shepherd – a winning combination.

There were other trials and tribulations during that first week, such as two sheep slipping down a large culvert that Network Rail had built to keep water off the train tracks, but nothing could really compare to the Beast from the East. We had had a baptism of ice, not fire.

Pig keeping has long been a tradition on Westmorland farms, and our new farmyard had a wonderful old piggery area with little houses and an exercise area for the pigs. We made a video of our new farm to show to my in laws after the snow had melted, and they insisted on buying us two pigs to keep in the piggery. A friend of ours near Rusland had a litter of piglets ready to be weaned, and Hector informed me that I had to go and pick up two pigs, Joyce and Jemima. They were both gilts, so we couldn't call them Jim and Joyce after my in laws.

I now know where the expression 'squealing like a pig' comes from. The noise that the pigs made when I brought them home and they did not want to get out of the trailer and into the piggery was unbelievable – eardrum piercing. Once we had metaphorically blocked our ears and pulled them out they set about exploring their piggery and destroying everything in sight; doorframes ripped off, mud churned up and chaos. Exactly like a pig should, they were as happy as proverbial pigs in muck.

The new piglets settling in.

I had never kept pigs before, so there was a lot of learning to do. They kept their house very clean, and enjoyed nuzzling into fresh straw and sleeping through the afternoons. I was quite nervous of them, as my friend's Dad had shown me various bite marks and scars that he had accumulated from a lifetime of pig keeping. They would certainly bite your wellies if you dared to go into their area without taking them any food.

Their two little faces stood at the gate waiting were enough to brighten everyone's day. Unfortunately my sons got them into the habit of expecting polos from all passers by, and they snorted at everyone in expectation as they approached. Joyce also liked a good scratch, Jemima was not so keen but would still come and say hello.

They were Gloucester Old Spot/Saddleback pigs, good old-fashioned pigs in an old fashioned piggery. Just what every farmyard needs. The other residents of the farmyard were my ancient ex battery hens Sally and Henny Penny. They strutted around the yard all day flashing their frilly knickers and scratching at every available surface. Despite being several years old, they each laid an egg each day and were quite the most entertaining animals on the farm.

April 2018

There are seasons when things go wrong,
and they just have to be lived through
Beatrix Potter (1928)

This chapter could very well be subtitled 'in which we learn from our mistakes'. Moving to a new farm always brings challenges for people and animals.

After the snow receded we got ready for lambing time. Our initial plan had been to move all the sheep back to the fields around Low Borrowbridge, but by the last week of March with lambing imminent the grass had not started to grow at all. Ideally sheep need at least 6cm of grass growth in this area for them to produce enough milk for their lambs. Spring was very delayed.

The best of the grass did actually seem to be around Low Park Farm. All the Herdwicks had settled happily there, so we decided to leave them there, and walk the Rough Fell Sheep and the Welsh Speckles back to Low Borrowbridge. We were hoping that because the Herdwicks were all older sheep and had lambed several times before, that lambing would be very straightforward for them, and they would not need assistance. It seemed a reasonable assumption to make, as generally fell sheep that cannot lamb by themselves are not kept for several years.

This would mean that we would be lambing in two

locations, one three and a half miles from the other, but there didn't seem to be much choice given the lack of grass. Getting down to Low Park Farm in the Land Rover was proving quite tricky in the wet, slippy mud. It is also not ideal as a small lambing trailer cannot be attached to it, so Hector took the decision to buy a quad bike. Once we had the Honda quad, nipping between the two locations became easier.

I had never driven a quad before, and found the prospect of driving down the track to Low Park Farm quite terrifying the first few times that I did it. There are three sections of track that are really steep, and covered in slippy gravel, and you are about two and a half miles from another road at this point.

Hector's car was in for repair, and he was using the Land Rover for work for a week, so I had no choice but to get on the quad and drive it. The weather was relentlessly wet, and the quad often felt like it was going sideways rather than forwards, but I had to learn to trust it. After the final steep hill to Low Park Farm there is a track above the River Lune. At this point you are about 300 feet above the river, with a very steep slope between you and the river. The quad slid about on the track, and I had to learn to trust it and drive confidently. I was not going to slip into the river. I had a job to do and I had to get on and do it.

Gradually I began to trust the quad and to realise what remarkable machines these are, and how they have revolutionised shepherding in the hills. There was no way that I, at the grand old age of 47, could cover all the miles I was required to do each day on foot. I have a health App on my phone, and even using the quad I was walking between ten

Waiting for hay.

and fifteen kilometres every day. To have to walk between locations would have made lambing in two locations impossible. Of course, I was shepherding what had been two separate farms, and countless small farms had been amalgamated in the hills to form larger farms. Sitting eating my lunch down at Low Park Farm enjoying the view before returning to Low Borrowbridge, it was easy to feel envious of an earlier time when the value of lamb was much higher and a small farm like Low Park could have provided for a family. Times change, but I enjoyed that small patch of heaven sitting in the deserted garden eating a sandwich.

Lambing the Herdwicks was not as straight forward as we had hoped. They had all been scanned for twins. Some had been killed under the fallen tree, and another two died after they had their annual Heptavac injection for various sheepy diseases before lambing. One sheep then prolapsed before lambing; this is when the sheep's vagina pops outwards instead of staying inside. It turns itself inside out and sticks out the back of the sheep. We put the prolapse back in, and put a harness on the sheep to prevent it from coming back out again. It was a very difficult sheep to catch after I noticed the prolapse, and it was very difficult to put the prolapse back in, and very frustrating when she died before she lambed. We had put her inside the barn, and she seemed fine, but about a week later she lay down and died. This was not the 'easy lambing' experience that we had been expecting.

Another Herdwick prolapsed while lambing. We brought her into the barn and I lambed her successfully, but then both lambs died suddenly. I think they were premature. Hector shot off in the car to one of the farms that he works at and returned with an orphan lamb. He skinned one of the dead lambs and put the skin onto the orphan lamb like a jacket, and thankfully the Herdwick accepted the lamb as her own. We then kept them inside a small pen for a couple of days to keep an eye on them, and once we were 100% sure that she loved the lamb as her own we let them outside. A success story of sorts.

I drove down to Low Park Farm every morning and evening. One morning I found one of the Herdwicks dolefully standing by a dead lamb. Knowing that they were all scanned for twins I caught the ewe and pulled out the second lamb that had one of its legs back and was stuck. Lambs should ideally be born like a diver, with the nose and two legs coming out. The first lamb seemed to have suffocated in the 'bag' that it was born in. At least the ewe had one live lamb to love.

At teatime I checked on the new mother, and was alarmed to see that she had mothered the lamb so much that she had bitten its tail off. The lamb was losing blood and was lying on the ground looking dopey. I took them back home in the trailer, bathed the tail stump in iodine, and put them in pen next to the other one with the adopted lamb. At this point we had four dead Herdwicks and two with one lamb each both in the 'hospital ward' inside the barn. What a start!

The next ewe to lamb had difficulty lambing and my son pulled two dead lambs out of her. She showed no interest in the dead lambs, so we didn't bother to try and adopt a new lamb onto her.

Checking every morning and evening I was surprised to see a ewe that I had seen in the morning at Low Borrowbridge in the farmyard one afternoon. She had lambed herself at Low Park Farm, and had then walked over three miles to get to Low Borrowbridge with her newborn lamb. She stood as proud as punch in the farmyard waiting for me to come out of the door and admire her lamb. Sheep are remarkable sometimes. I don't know what had happened to her other lamb, but I was very impressed that she had found the farmhouse after only moving there a couple of weeks before and walking such a distance. How she negotiated a couple of fences and walls with a newborn lamb we will never know.

Once this remarkable ewe had lambed our luck seemed to change. The rest of the Herdwicks lambed themselves, unaided, and looked after two healthy lambs. Thank goodness.

We decided that we had to scale back our expectations of the Herdwicks in the future. Perhaps the previous owner had been over ambitious with the tup he had used. In their natural habitat on the fells Herdwicks usually lamb one pure bred lamb unaided. Had we expected too much of them to lamb two meaty lambs unaided? In the future we will bring any expecting twins closer to the house, and perhaps not encourage them to have twins.

A sheep's fertility can be boosted just before tupping time by 'flushing'. This is when the sheep are put onto very good grass just before they meet the tup and conceive their lambs. Their body is then inclined to conceive twins, as the expectation is that they will have good grass throughout their pregnancy. Perhaps it would be wiser not to 'flush' the Herdwicks, and not to use such a chunky tup. We live and learn.

Meanwhile whilst the Herdwicks were lambing at Low Park Farm I was busy lambing the Ouessant sheep inside the sheep shed. Ouessants are the world's smallest breed of sheep. Hobby keepers, estate owners and rare breeds enthusiasts love them, as they are tiny, pretty sheep. I had fourteen to lamb this year, plus four young hoggs that had not been with the tup. I had brought them all inside during the snow.

Ouessants only ever have one lamb due to their tiny size. Ten of the ewes had gone to Millican Dalton, my tup from Borrowdale in the Lake District, which I had used for the last three years. He is such a tiny, furious chap and very feisty. His favourite trick is to knock you over by running at the back of your knees when you least expect it. Feistiness is a great trait in a tup, as long as you can physically contain him. I had thought that he was going to break through the back window of the Land Rover when I bought him and transported him home in it. He had also greeted me in the sheep pens at his farm by charging at me and trying to knock me over.

The four shearling Ouessant sheep, the first time lambers at two years old, had gone to a different tup as they are Millican's daughters. This was a younger, much quieter tup.

The Ouessants began to lamb, quietly, in the straw in the barn. Steadily, stealthily they lambed in succession looking after their tiny lambs. Once they had lambed I put them in a pen with their lamb. Once the lamb started escaping from the pen and running around the barn I put them out into the back garden where I could keep an eye on them from the kitchen. Once I had to dash out waving my arms and shouting as two lambs, left alone temporarily while their mothers were eating, were being dive bombed by two crows. The lambs are so tiny and vulnerable that they do need keeping an eye on.

After about two weeks ten of the Ouessants had lambed and I had nine gimmer (girl) lambs and one tup (boy) lamb. This will give me a real opportunity to expand my flock. Selling without any problem at £60 for a castrated male sheep, £100 for a tup and £300 for a gimmer lamb they are also the most profitable sheep on the farm. Good things do come in small packages. The only disappointment was that only one of the shearlings that went to the younger tup had lambed. I wondered, perhaps rather optimistically, if they would lamb a bit later than the rest as they may have come into season as quickly as the older sheep when put in with the tup.

I decided to put the hoggs outside as well, but as I lifted one of them up I noticed that she had milk. The next day she lambed a tiny, perfect gimmer lamb. I had never had an Ouessant without a mothering instinct before, but this one hated the lamb. I fed the lamb off one of the other Ouessants that had just lambed and had plenty of colostrum, and hoped that she would accept her. Sadly there was no way that this 'teenage Mum' was going to accept her lamb. It would not have been sensible to adopt her onto another Ouessant, due to their small size they cannot feed twins, so it looked like she was going to be my first ever orphan Ouessant.

Our oldest Ouessant, Ella, who was nine years old, also had a gimmer lamb. She was in the next pen. The last couple of months of relentless rain had taken their toll and she

Ouessant orphan lamb.

sadly died, slipping away with her lamb cuddled up next to her. I took both lambs and put them into a warm area filled with comfy straw. At least they now had each other. Both of them took to bottle-feeding quickly. They were so tiny that getting them to have the right amount of milk and not overfeeding them was going to be tricky. Twice I feared that they were 'bloated' and fed them olive oil. This was when I put them onto a self-feeding bucket system. I decided that I would have to feed them small, regular feeds myself from a bottle. The routine of four hourly feeds for five weeks began. At that point they were my only orphan lambs.

One night I went out to do a 2am feed and I could hear a lamb crying in the field behind the barn. It sounded desperate so I got a headtorch and went to investigate. The sight that met my eyes was much more horrific than I could have imagined. My five Welsh sheep had lambed easily, four gimmers and a tup lamb. I was really pleased with the tup lamb as he was definitely a show quality lamb and potential tup, and all the girls looked well. It was dark and very stormy that night, and the gates to the slurry pit had snapped their string fastening and blown open. One of the Welsh ewes was drowning in the slurry pit, and the lambs were stood around her on the 'crust' and hadn't yet sunk in.

The slurry pit is a large storage tank that the cow effluent that collects in the cow building is contained in. When the cows are inside during the winter the waste is scraped into the tank by tractor, then it can be spread on the fields to fertilise them. As the farm had been empty for a while the slurry was still left in the tank from the previous year, and a crust had grown on top of it, so it looked just like a grassy field.

We had never had a slurry pit before but I was aware of the dangers of them having heard of people, cows and horses drowning in them. I was absolutely mortified that I had let this happen. I had obviously not been vigilant enough in checking the fastening. This is farming, you make a mistake and things die.

I had to act quickly. I called the lambs but they would not leave the sinking ewe. I could not get to her. If I stepped on the crust I would sink. I tried to reach the lambs with my shepherd's crook but couldn't.

I ran inside and woke Hector. He was very sleepy, but jumped out of bed and ran around the back of the slurry pit in the wind and the rain. He wondered if he could reach them through the cow area, but could not. There was a little ledge at the back of the cow area overhanging the slurry pit, and he jumped onto it across the slurry. I thought that I was going to be sick with the anxiety of the situation, but he kept reassuring me that he was safe. With his stick he frightened the lambs away from the ewe. I then hooked them with my stick out the side of the pit, and breathed a sigh of relief.

The ewe that had drowned needed her lamb feeding, so I took the lamb into the kitchen to give her a bottle, which she gratefully took. She would have to join the other orphans now. I decided to wipe some of the slurry off her face, and this bathing in the sink was a trauma too far. She suddenly went floppy in my arms. She had stopped breathing. Hector had gone back to bed now. I laid her on the floor, her heart was still beating. I had been trained in first aid when I was a teacher, and that training kicked into action. I gave her some breaths and thankfully she came back to life. I carefully carried her outside into the barn and put her with the two Ouessants. It would take me a while to come to terms with the fact that my negligence had killed her mother, but at least she was alive.

After the Welsh and the Herdwicks we had the Rough Fell Sheep and a few mules to lamb, along with the Ryeland crosses. I had kept Shetland sheep several years ago, but the boy lambs were too small to be commercial, selling at only £1 each at auction (exactly the cost of the ear tags required to take them to the auction). To try and make the Shetlands more profitable I had stopped breeding them pure and crossed them to a coloured (brown) Ryeland tup. The lambs were then Shetland/Ryeland crosses and I sold the female sheep to smallholders who came on my sheep keeping courses as an ideal 'starter sheep', and sold the boy lambs at auction as store lambs. They made £19 each, a big improvement on the Shetland boys.

This year I had kept ten of these Shetland/Ryeland crosses, and used a pedigree white Ryeland tup on them. I was really pleased to see them lamb easily in turn. From the ten ewes we had eleven lambs. Ten of the lambs were Ryeland, as planned, and one was a Rough Fell – how I am not sure. I also planned to produce knitting wool from the Shetland/Ryeland fleeces, to further add value to the sheep. All in all, the Ryeland cross sheep had done well and I was pleased with them.

That just left the Roughs and the mules. We don't have many mule sheep as they are really out of our price range. In order to get the best out of mule sheep you also need to invest in a 'terminal sire' such as a Texel tup. The few that we had were ex-pet lambs that had been given to me to look after in previous years. There is a saying that a pet lamb cannot make a good mother, as she has not been mothered herself. Generally we have found this not to be true in the past. I had put the mules to the Welsh tup to try and produce some stocky, hardy lambs. One died, for no apparent reason, one had twins and rejected one but raised the other successfully, and the third did not lamb. So from keeping these three mules over the winter we managed to produce one lamb. This probably backs up the saying that a pet lamb cannot be a good mother.

The Rough Fell sheep had had a very hard winter. They had to move farms in the middle of a terrible episode of weather, and adapt to life at an altitude of 1,000 feet higher than where they had lived for the rest of their lives. The weather had been relentlessly wet, then snowy and windy. My expectations of the Rough Fell lambs were not great. They were lambing later than the Herdwicks and the other sheep because the tup had had an accident just before he was due to be released to the ewes. He fell down a crag face when on the scent of a heifer in season and sprained his leg, so he had been on antibiotics and rest, and was put in with the ewes later than planned.

They started lambing on the 8th April and three out of the first four to lamb had lovely sets of twins, with the other having a single. Another thirteen Roughs lambed quickly and all had good single lambs. The size of some of the lambs was astonishing. It just shows how resilient sheep can be, having lived through a terrible winter and then producing a cracking lamb unaided.

I was quite excited for what my two 'Rough Diamond' purchases would have. One had been born in 2015 and one in 2016 at the sale of individual 'Rough Diamond' sheep which are the best examples of the breed. The first Rough Diamond, called Harry after the man who bred her, had a most enormous single tup lamb. I was hoping for a gimmer but could not grumble at the size and quality of the lamb. It was also very nicely marked with a lovely face.

The second Rough Diamond had been named Margot by Bryn Thompson, one of my followers on Twitter who was always very supportive of my ventures on the farm. I had actually got the money to buy Margot from selling knitwear that Twitter followers such as Bryn kindly purchased. I was waiting for a great photo opportunity to show the followers, who had in effect purchased the sheep, Margot's lamb. I could see the day before she lambed that she was getting ready, nesting, so I was up early poised with my camera ready for the big reveal.

When I first saw her standing in the field I didn't realise anything was wrong, but as I got closer I realised that she had a lamb's head, and no legs, hanging out behind her as she pootled along. I knew that I would have one chance to catch her, so rattled a feedbag and leapt off the quad towards her, grabbing a horn and trying to upend her. She really was the most enormous sheep, and refused to go down on the ground. I grabbed one of her back legs whilst holding onto her horn (quite a feat given the size of her) and it took me six attempts to upend her.

The lamb was well and truly stuck. I found its legs and pulled them forward but I could see that it was dead. I pulled the lamb out and realised that something was really wrong with it, and it would not have survived however it was born. It had what can only be described as holes in its abdomen, with its intestines on the outside of its body instead of inside. It was also black, not black and white as a Rough Fell usually is.

Margot showed not the slightest bit of interest in the lamb. If she was keen to mother it I would have found her a lamb to adopt, but at this moment she did not have any mothering instinct, so I let her go.

As I pulled the lamb out blood from its body had splashed me all over my face. I also had one arm covered in blood where I had checked inside to make sure that she was not having another lamb. I parked the quad and walked back to the farmhouse covered in blood carrying the dead lamb in a bucket. Mum, Dad and my husband were waiting to have lunch.

"OK?" asked my husband.

"Yes, I'm OK" I said. "I've just had a bit of a disappointing morning." I ate my soup letting the disappointment sink in, and then rallied myself to go back down to Low Park Farm where I had spotted another ewe that looked like she was going to lamb. My job at lambing time is to focus on the living, not the dead, and to make sure that as many lambs as possible survive. Sadness can be acknowledged, but cannot become all encompassing. The shepherd must remain positive and focussed on the sheep and lambs that are alive and not dwell on those that are lost.

Our lambing percentage between 2014-2017 had been 110%, 123%, 120%, and 124%. This means that each ewe had produced 1.1, 1.2, 1.2 and 1.2 lambs on average. We don't encourage our sheep to have a very high percentage as historically we have not had very good grass to feed them on. This year, despite the 'Beast from the East' and moving farms, we managed 115%. When we started lambing it looked like our lambing percentage would be a lot lower, less than 100%, which would be a disaster financially.

We had survived. We lived to fight another year. I don't write 'survived' lightly, as at times this year it did feel like a battle to keep our heads not above water, but above the drifting snow.

May 2018

Marking Day on 12th May is traditionally the day on which cattle are turned out onto commons to graze, as good weather can generally be expected from now. Co incidentally, this 12th May was also the day on which we marked our lambs.

In order for the meadows to grow successfully and produce either hay or silage they need to be grazed by livestock over the winter months. This is so that the animals will fertilise the meadow with their dung, and also help seeds germinate by breaking up the soil with their feet.

Most meadows contain good grass and are used in Cumbria for lambing, so towards the end of lambing the sheep and lambs must be moved off the good grass and onto a common or rough grazing to allow the meadow to be 'shut up' to grow. Traditionally before the lambs are moved they are 'marked'. This means that they are marked with their owner's flock mark, and on fell farms their ears would have been notched as well to show which farm they belonged to. A notch would be taken out of the ear with some special pliers (e.g., heart shaped hole in the middle of the left ear). This is an age-old tradition so that animals in shared grazing on the commons can be identified.

Our new flock mark was inherited with the farm and is a red line along the right hand side of the sheep. The ewes and tups were already marked, so our job was to gather the sheep and lambs from four meadows into a large pen, worm them and mark the lambs. The lambs and ewes would then be transported in tandem in three trips down to Low Park Farm – the sheep in the sheep trailer being towed by the Land Rover followed by the lambs in the trailer pulled by the quad. Some of the lambs were still very tiny and we did not want them to get crushed in the trailer.

The lambs and ewes in each load would then be put together into the sheep pens at Low Park Farm, and when we were sure that they had all 'mothered up' with the correct lambs, released into the grazing.

The day started well as it was bright and sunny, and the sheep looked happy and relaxed. We hoped that we would be able to get a lot done, and decided to gather in the hoggs first to check their feet, worm them if necessary and shear any fleeces that were tatty and 'rooing' (coming off). This also gave us a good opportunity to check our boy lambs from last year. They were nearly ready to be taken to the abattoir, at almost exactly a year old. We decided to check them again the following week.

The gimmer hoggs were looking well and we decided to take them down to Low Park Farm as well. The first load of the day set off. Meanwhile whilst the boys were taking the hoggs down I began to gather the sheep and the lambs. I was quite pleased that when they returned I had over half of them gathered into a small strip of land with a big pen at the end.

The day had started well. It took us a while longer to get all the others in, but by dinnertime all the sheep and lambs were in the pens. The Saturday steam train steaming through the farm reminded us that we had better go inside for our dinner and eat before we carried on with our afternoon jobs.

There were a few missing faces in the sheep pens. What with the deaths in the culvert, the slurry pit incident, the falling trees, the bad weather, prolapsing and dying, we have lost about 20% of our flock this year. There is no denying it has been a very long, hard winter for the sheep. However, those that were still here looked in good fettle. Some had scraggy fleeces because they had been in poor condition and then come good. This can often cause the

fleece to fall off and is generally a good sign (as long as that really is the reason that the fleece is coming out, and it is not sheep scab or lice or something grizzly).

The sheep had never been on such good grass, and while they were looking well they also had messy bums from the rich diet. The messy fleece must be trimmed away from around their bums or it can attract flies that lay maggots. The process of clipping bottoms in this way is called 'dagging' and is one of the worst jobs of the year.

Before long the sheep were dagged and wormed, and the lambs marked. The Welsh sheep were taken off to a small field near the house as I wanted people to see them on the farm walks, and the others were taken down to Low Park Farm.

I had to dash off and leave the boys to transport the sheep as I was collecting some ex-battery hens at 4.30pm. I had just bought five new hens when I received a text from Fresh Start for Hens that I had rehomed ex-battery hens from before, asking if I could take some. They desperately needed new homes for thousands of hens so I said I would take 14 as 20 could fit into the hut.

The hens were collected from a back garden in Kendal and on the way home I popped into the supermarket to get some food for tea. The hens were secured inside three boxes in the back of the car. When I came out of the supermarket I was surprised to see hens stood on the car seats looking like they were ready to drive off. I was surprised there had not been a supermarket announcement "Can the owner of the car full of hens please return to their vehicle?"

When I got home the sheep were all safely mothered up with their lambs at Low Park Farm so I put the hens into the hut and turned my attention to two renegade sheep that had evaded capture earlier in the day.

I left a lot of gates open into the yard, and sure enough later I saw the sheep running past the kitchen window and into the farmyard. I nipped out to shut them into the yard and contain them, but to my horror the gate onto the road outside had been left open. My son had flown out of the gate in a hurry when he received a text saying that his bosses' wife had gone into labour, and asking if he could go over to their farm and keep an eye on things.

I managed to sprint past the sheep and shut the gate just in time, and then managed to get them into a corner of the yard and catch them. The sheep pens in the yard were out of action as they were occupied by visiting miscreant sheep that had been brought back from Low Park Farm earlier and were waiting for their owners to collect them. The two sheep and their lambs were then taken down to Low Park Farm, leaving only the Ouessants and the best Welsh sheep at Low Borrowbridge to show to visitors on our farm walks.

After marking day the farmyard seemed very quiet. There were no lambs, ewes, cows or calves about. There were only hot, dry meadows surrounding the house on all sides. My sons took advantage of the hot weather and began harrowing the fields. This process removes any dead plant matter from the meadow and allows the rest of it to photosynthesise more efficiently. It also smooths out any lumps and bumps that have been made during the winter.

It took seven hours to chain harrow the meadow around the house the following day. It is a monotonous job and one tractor broke down in the process, but by the end of the weekend we had achieved a lot. We had marked and moved the lambs, and harrowed the meadows. All that remained was for us to get a text telling us that a baby had been born, and it would have been a successful weekend all round.

I suppose it's the same for anyone who takes on a new job or business, but at this time I seemed to lurch from success to disaster from day to day. Some days were good days when things went well, and then other days were not successful largely due to my naivity.

As an example, in the week following marking day I was on my own at the farm just about all week during the day, apart from my parents coming over to help one day with clearing out the old buildings and sorting things out in the farmyard on Thursday. I decided to have an afternoon out on Wednesday afternoon, largely because I had only spoken to the lady in the post office and had no other real conversation that week. It was Mungrisedale Shepherd's meet, the first shepherds' meet of the year and a Swaledale sheep show.

Looking at a map I decided that I could incorporate the shepherds' meet into my afternoon school run, it would add about 30 minutes to my travelling time, but I love watching sheep shows and there were sure to be people that I knew to chat to there. When I arrived at Mungrisedale, which is at the foot of Blencathra, it was a perfect May afternoon. The verges were bursting with wildflowers as I walked over the wooden bridge by the inn, and along the lane to the sheep show. I could hear swallows chattering above me, and the beck gushing along next to me, and shortly the hubbub of the shepherds meet as people looked at the sheep and chatted over a cup of tea in the sun.

It was the perfect afternoon in the Lake District, and what's more I felt like a member of a secret club. While others toiled away in offices and classrooms here we were, looking at sheep in the sun. What a privilege to be here in this tiny field hidden away in a Lakeland valley.

The next day, however, some of the magic was lost and I felt extremely stupid after making a naive mistake. Some scrap metal collectors had come round previously, and we had been saving a big pile of scrap metal up for them, adding old gates etc. to the pile until there was a lorry load for them to take away. They arrived back to collect it, and were very chatty and polite. Mum was watching them load the lorry, instructed to by Dad, but I said that I was sure they were trustworthy and to come inside for some lunch.

I told the scrap metal men that we were going to have our lunch, and they said that they would come and tell me how much it was worth once they had finished loading it. I went and sat down at the kitchen table and after a couple of minutes the lorry shot past the kitchen window and out of the yard. I ran to the kitchen door but it was too late they had gone.

I was quite upset that they had taken all the metal without leaving any money, but later in the afternoon I was really upset to see that not only had they taken about 400m of fencing wire that I asked them not to touch, but they had also left a large industrial sized fridge freezer lying in the field. Fly tipping on our land. I was very cross with myself for being so stupid and trusting them unsupervised in the farmyard. A lesson learnt, the hard way. I now had the problem of how to remove a huge industrial fridge from the corner of the field. Good days and bad days.

At the end of lambing time it is traditional to have a Lambing Service in the local church to thank God for the lambs that have been born that year. Previously we have always enjoyed the lambing service at Hawkshead, so we were pleased to see that there was to be a Lambing Service at Howgill Church.

Howgill Church is a little country church about five miles down the lane from our house. What I love about the church, apart from its location that is absolutely idyllic beside a little stream surrounded by yew trees, is that in the graveyard many of the gravestones have engraved animals on, showing the farmers' passions. There is one with a Rough Fell sheep, one with a Swaledale and one with a Border collie.

It was a bright beautiful day as we joined with our neighbours at the Lambing Service. A lamb and a ewe were penned up outside the church. There was a wedding going to be held there in two weeks time, and the local people had been fundraising to get the church looking smart for the wedding. It had very recently been repainted and had a brand new carpet down ready for the service. The church was full; the only pew left was right at the front so we sat there.

To begin the service Fiona, a local shepherdess, read out a poem that she had written about lambing time. The poem concluded with the marking, tailing and castrating of lambs, and the vicar asks if everybody had finished lambing. We then sang *All things bright and beautiful,* except that the verses have been changed to be all about lambing.

The little lambs so tender,

The faithful feisty ewe,
The gangs of gamb'lin playmates
So full of life that's new
The eager tup in autumn
The barn stuffed full of hay
Our winter's work of mending
Throughout God's gifted day

There were several readings about lambs, and Jesus being the good shepherd, and then some prayers for our farms.

For the friendship and support of our communities,
For the beauty of the hills and valleys
We thank you, Father.

For the changing weather and seasons,
The dawns and sunsets and the starry nights
We thank you, Father.

For the fields and pastures which provide food for our flocks
And water from stream or river
We thank you, Lord.

For our ewes, with their own wisdom,
For their strength and care as mothers
We thank you, Lord.

For lambs, for the miracle of their birth
And for the bounding joy of their young life
We thank you, Lord.

We pray that our lambs may be free from sickness,
And safe from attack by animals and birds.

We pray that all who care for the sheep

may be givenwisdom and endurance
And may receive a just reward for their work.
I may be wrong, but I can think of no other profession that

has special church services in their community to pray and thank God for their livelihood. Events like this show how vital shepherding is to our cultural heritage in Cumbria. It is also a great way in which to both celebrate shepherding and share our anxieties with our neighbours. I loved the way that we prayed for 'ewes with their own wisdom', valuing the vital role that our hefted flocks have in our businesses and landscapes.

At the end of the service we prayed that we would have "the grace to conserve, for those who come after, the beauty of our landscape, the traditions of our people and the strength of our local community." This is every farming family's prayer, that we may have the strength to keep on keeping on, and that someone will follow us. Everything we do is with quiet optimism; every stone wall that is repaired is done so in the hope that somebody will be there to do the same job in the next generation. Generations of sheep follow each other on the farms, and generations of farming families.

We are right at the beginning of our family's journey at Low Borrowbridge, but everything we do is a continuation of what has been done before. Things will be repaired and maintained with reverence and respect for those who have worked here before, with the hope that someone will 'come after'.

In order to understand the present and plan for the future, the past must be understood. In order to plan for the future at Low Borrowbridge, I must first understand the first two thousand years of history on this site, so I set about trying to learn as much as I could about Low Borrowbridge.

History and Geography

History and geography are all around you at Low Borrow-bridge. As soon as you step out of the kitchen door you are confronted by physical geography, human geography and history.

The farm is set in a narrow gorge between high fells. It is built where the Borrow Beck that flows down through Westmorland Borrowdale, meets the River Lune. The source of the Lune is at Adamthwaite, near Ravenstonedale in the Howgills, and it meanders through the farm along the valley bottom.

The sides of the valleys are filled with fields and ancient woodland, most notably the heart shaped wood that is a landmark for those travelling through the gorge. The fells to the west of the valley are part of the Lake District National Park, and to the east the Howgills are part of the Yorkshire Dales National Park.

Set on top of this dramatic physical geography is the human geography of today's busy world. The M6 motorway and the west coast mainline railway both pass through the valley, along with numerous fast jets and big slow planes on RAF exercises. The motorway dominates the valley, and this stretch of motorway is generally thought to be both the most dramatic and beautiful stretch of motorway in the UK.

The dramatic geography is equalled by the history of the valley which for centuries has been the main western

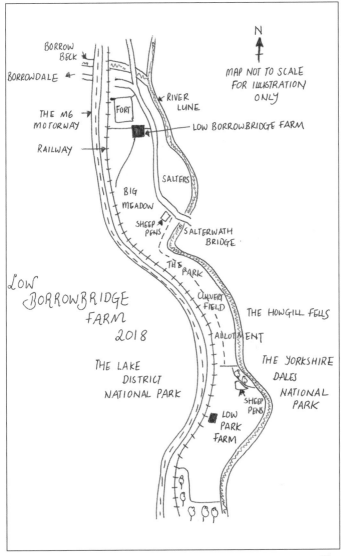

route between England and Scotland, and the border has at some points in history been in the valley itself.

In order to understand the history of the valley we must begin at the beginning. I must acknowledge at this point that my understanding of the farm has been greatly enhanced by both the Lunesdale Archaeological Trust and the book *Low Borrowbridge* (2016) by Graham Hooley, Jan Hicks and Judith Anstee. It is not often that you buy a property and are given a proper, academic book about the history of the place. It really was a great help in understanding my new surroundings.

Beginning at the beginning, as far as we can, there was a prehistoric site from the Bronze or Iron Age at High Carlingill, which is half a mile down the valley from here. Following on from this there was a general abandonment of large areas of the uplands of Northern Britain, until the rush of action in Roman Britain as they sought to add new lands and territories to their empire.

When the Romans invaded Britain in 43AD the north west region was populated by people that they called the Brigantes. The Romans built the road that today we call the Fairmile Road (as it is a straight, flat, fair mile for racing fell ponies) that goes through the farm. It was built as a road for the troops advancing into northern Britain to use, and was the main route through the west of the country. Of great interest to me is the fact that as the troops advanced north through the country they saw our stocky little ponies, the forefathers and mothers of the Fell Ponies, living in the Howgills today.

A Roman fort was constructed at Low Borrowbridge to control the flow of people in the Lune Gorge. It is on a raised piece of land so that it commands a view of the valley north and south and would be very difficult to attack. If you stand on the site of the fort today, and watch the trains on the railway line and the cars and lorries on the motorway heading north and south through the valley, you can see that the gorge has always been an important site for the movement of people.

The current fort covers an area of 2.7 acres, although it is thought that this stone built fort replaced an earlier wooden fort. A lot of the stone from the fort has been plundered and used to build our farmhouse, and some railway cottages that have since been demolished. There is also a Roman cemetery near the river, and a possible *mansio* house in what is now the garden of the farmhouse. This *mansio* also has a bath house. It is believed that the fort was occupied from 70AD to 400AD. There has never been conclusive evidence to confirm the name of the fort in Roman times, although most historians believe from lists of marching times that have been found, that the fort was called Alone.

The name Alone makes sense, as it would be from this name that the River Lune got its name. Alone could have easily changed to Lune over time. Alone could be seen as a slightly ironic name now for one of the busiest valleys in northern Britain in terms of transport, but it is still a very quiet and lonely place away from the motorway. Apart from weekend cyclists and one or two neighbours nobody passes by the house each day as I work there. When I am at Low Park Farm, about three miles from the nearest road that I can access, despite the trains and motorway traffic whizzing past a couple of hundred meters away, I feel alone.

Low Borrowbridge was definitely occupied in the medieval period, and would have been used for sheep and cattle grazing. The house from this period has not been found, but it is most likely that it is under the current buildings and incorporated into them.

The Lancaster to Carlisle railway was built through the valley in the 1840s. It took a significant amount of grazing land and meadow out of production, and also provided another source of income for the farm as a 'navvies bar' was built at the back of the farmhouse, then a coaching inn, to serve the workers. One of the main engineers of the railway, James Day, lived at Low Borrowbridge for over 40 years, from 1853 to 1894.

The farm was obviously in existence as both a farm and an inn when the railway was built, but when was the farmhouse actually built? The farm is marked on a map of Westmorland in 1770, and we found a coin dating from 1742 in the floorboards of the house. The first mention of the inn is in 1721 in a will, where somebody is described as an 'innkeeper from Borrowbridge'. The inn was con-

LOW BORROWBRIDGE FARMHOUSE 16th CENTURY

veniently placed for traffic, both for those travelling on horseback or walking with animals. There is mention of Borrowbridge in a will of 1601, but it is not definitely clear

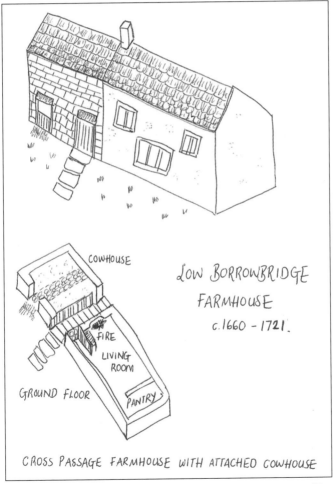

COWHOUSE

LOW BORROWBRIDGE
FARMHOUSE
c. 1660 – 1721.

FIRE

LIVING ROOM

GROUND FLOOR

PANTRY

CROSS PASSAGE FARMHOUSE WITH ATTACHED COWHOUSE

whether it is this house that is being referred to.

Having lived in the house, and in the old farmhouse at The Syke that dated from 1565, my belief is that the rear of the house is a sixteenth century farmhouse, similar to the sixteenth century part of Thorneythwaite Farm in Borrowdale and Bird Howe in Eskdale. That is a two-storey house of about sixteen feet square (ours was 17ft x 15ft); there was usually an outside staircase to get to the upper room (or quite often a ladder within so that the family were safe from possible marauders). The roofs were made of slate but may have been thatched with bracken initially. If you stand outside and look carefully at the construction of the house you can see that this block has initially been a detached house.

This small building was then modified, as living standards improved changed, into a cross passage farmhouse with attached cowhouse. This was a design of farmhouse that was very popular from 1660-1790. The house was attached to the farm building where the cows were kept. The farmer could get access to his cows from the house without going outside, but the living accommodation is separated from the cowhouse by a passage with a door at either end crossing the house. This living accommodation is today our farm kitchen, and the cowhouse is the boot room.

The coaching inn, which seems to have been in existence in 1721, but definitely by 1770, was built at right angles to the older house, with the pantry connecting the two. The pantry also seems to have been the division between the owners' accommodation and the guest's accommodation in the coaching inn. There are sliding windows in the pantry for people to pay their bill before they left. At some point the additional two bedrooms and the 'court room' have been built on the end. The court room is so named as disputes in the local area were settled here.

Low Park Farm is also marked on the 1770 map of Westmorland, although it is not clear wether the current house dates from this period. It was last inhabited before the building of the motorway, exactly 50 years ago, when it was compulsorily purchased. The land at Low Park Farm was added to in compensation for the land lost to the mo-

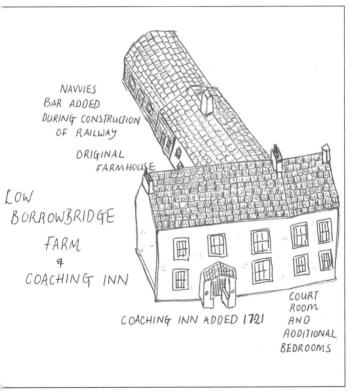

NAVVIES BAR ADDED DURING CONSTRUCTION OF RAILWAY

ORIGINAL FARMHOUSE

LOW BORROWBRIDGE FARM & COACHING INN

COACHING INN ADDED 1721

COURT ROOM AND ADDITIONAL BEDROOMS

torway.

When I was travelling around Cumbria delivering and collecting boys from various places, I made a point of visiting any farms with diversification businesses in order to consider what might be best for our farm. I visited Yew Tree Barn, that sells reclaimed items and gifts and has a coffee shop, Low Sizergh farm shop and café, and also a heritage centre with café started by a farming family in the Dales. Anything is possible, but what all these businesses have in common are places to eat and drink. It is perhaps fortunate that my youngest son wants to work in catering when he leaves school.

Set amongst dramatic physical geography, next to a vital north/south route for both road and rail, Low Borrowbridge farm has a long history as a place both to travel through, and to live, farm and capitalise on diversification opportunities as they arrive. The Romans lived here in a fort for hundreds of years, and the farm with its associated diversifications into inn keeping and bar-tending, has been in existence since at least the sixteenth century. It is now up to us to decide on the next chapter for the farm. How will the farm business be structured? What diversification will be best, and what is the future of the Low Park Farm buildings are all questions that we need to work out as a family. Understanding some of the past, and learning more as we go along, will help to inform us and plan for the future.

June 2018

I think my city friends would agree that the view from this window today is much more satisfying than the morning paper. It presents no nerve-strain, no frustrations.

Dudley Hoys, *Below Scafell,* (1955)

2018 is a difficult time in which to plan for the future of a farming business. Brexit is looming, with no clear way ahead. It seems, although we don't actually know this for sure, that farming subsidies will be cut. There is much chatter in the media about 'public money for public goods' and natural capital. Natural capital requires farmers not just to produce food but to consider air quality, wildlife habitat, flood management and carbon sequestration amongst other concerns, such as improving land for wildlife and encouraging pollinators onto the farm.

A lot of farmers are unhappy about the emphasis on 'natural capital' and insist that the primary focus for the future must be food production. Whilst I would love the consumer to value hill bred beef and lamb, and be willing to pay for its free-range lifestyle like they do now for free range chicken, I am not disheartened by the focus on 'natural capital'.

It remains to be seen what will actually happen post Brexit, but if 'natural capital' is valued then farmers in the Yorkshire Dales and Lake District national parks are ideally placed to deliver it. We maintain stunningly beautiful landscapes that the public love to walk, run, bike, fish and swim through. On a sunny Saturday afternoon I counted 120 cyclists passing right past our farmhouse door and through the farm along the Fairmile Road. This 'natural capital' for enjoyment, relaxation and mental health of the nation is something we can deliver. How it will be quantified and what monetary value can be assigned to farmers for maintaining it remains to be seen. Schemes are currently being trialled in some areas of the Yorkshire Dales.

I refuse to believe that the upland farmers will be forgotten about in the new farming system, as many people seem to fear. Without any subsidy a lot of farms would not be able to continue, but surely it is better to pay us a subsidy to maintain the landscape in the way in which thousands of visitors love, than to stop hill farmers working and pay them unemployment benefits instead? Many hill farmers are happy to work 365 days a year for very little money, because their main priority in life is not making money but preserving their way of life and keeping their farm going. I believe it is vital for both the mental health of these farming families and the cultural heritage of our rural communities, for the government to maintain these hill farms.

I know that there are other sectors of employment such as fishing and mining where the industry has been closed to the detriment of the community. But when farmers are vital in maintaining a landscape that millions of visitors enjoy I think that hill farms are worth preserving. It may be that our main source of income comes from providing 'natural capital' and not from food production, but I do not have a problem with this as it would allow us to focus on preserving quality flocks of hill bred sheep and maintaining their genetic diversity that is crucial to the stratified sheep system in the UK.

After writing this passage I stumbled across a piece of writing in the book *Kendal Rough Fell Sheep* (2007) where the future of our farm is discussed by the previous owners. The book states:

> With John's son, Jonathan, working on the farm the future should have been secure. It is difficult to ask a young man to take on the unremitting workload, in the face of political interference and criticism, for the benefit of those with more leisure time than the owner.
>
> Essentially the family has no interest in being park keepers or working to fulfil other people's agendas. In spite of a love of wildlife, they too have always seen themselves as first and foremost, as good stockmen and farmers and their guardianship of the heritage is drawing to its inevitable close.

I guess you could say we have different views on being paid to provide 'natural capital', whilst we have very similar philosophies on farming alongside nature. This could be because I have not been brought up on a farm, but around those who love visiting Cumbria and walking in the hills. We have also bought two lots of the farm that have no public access, whereas some of the other lots had a 'right to roam' as they are classified as fell land. I can see that having people roaming wherever they like over your land can cause problems if you are trying to get a job done.

At Low Park Farm, an area with no public access, we have been thwarted in our attempts to gather sheep by both a loose dog running around without an owner, and a walker with a dog off the lead (indeed without a lead with them).

Some sort of scheme where farms are encouraged to ensure the continuity of the hill breeds and not cross them with a terminal sire to produce a 'butcher's lamb' would be ideal. This would have to sit hand in hand with a marketing campaign that encouraged the consumer to value 'free range' lamb and beef, showing the way that it is produced over large swathes of upland Britain. Surely it cannot be a difficult job to sell the idea of iconic sheep breeds in their local environment to the consumer?

We all remember the catchy slogan 'New Zealand lamb, your first choice any day' from the 1970s. Something like an image of a Swaledale sheep in the Yorkshire Dales with the slogan 'Swaledale lamb, raised for you in God's Own Country', 'Herdwick lamb, raised for generations in the Lake District fells', 'Rough Fell lamb, hardy, resilient and bred for you by generations of Cumbrian farmers', 'Cheviot lamb, free ranging in the hills of Northumberland for generations'... I could go on. Surely it cannot be too hard to sell these images to the public?

A balance between top quality hill flocks and the maintenance of our landscapes for the public to enjoy would be the ultimate package. This would allow the farmers to focus on the health and quality of their flocks, and perhaps boost local shows and shepherds' meets that are so crucial to the cultural heritage of the area. The public could also be made more aware of these events and take part in amateur stock judging and other fun competitions such as novelty dog shows. Nobody wants to hide our culture and keep it for ourselves, we want to share it with the world and encourage people to value our produce and our landscape. Simply driving through the Lake District on holiday it is hard to imagine the passion involved in farming here. If visitors go to Keswick tup fair and see the winner of the Edmondson Cup, or go to Grasmere Sports and see the winner of the senior Guides race, the passion and pride in our culture is proudly on display.

In the meantime we must work with the current system although the end of it is in sight, and make our living as best we can. There are two main streams of income from the Government that we can tap into. The first is the Basic Payment Scheme. At our previous farm I had to wait several years before joining the scheme as I had to first buy the 'entitlements' to join it. People often complain about farmers receiving this 'subsidy', but it is actually quite costly to join. It costs about a year's income to join the scheme, so you don't benefit for two years after joining it as the subsidy is paid in December for the year – if the Rural Payments Agency can process the claim efficiently. I received my first payment on 30 September of the following year, making it nearly three years until I saw any benefit from joining the scheme.

The second income opportunity is the Countryside Stewardship scheme, which is the environmental payment. The previous five-year agreement was just running out when we bought the farm, so I sent off for a pack. At first I could not see any significant benefit in joining the scheme as the majority of the land around the farm is a Scheduled Ancient Monument and there were very limited options available for the Roman fort and surrounding areas. Hopefully it will be beneficial for us to join the scheme, it is something that I must put some time and effort into understanding during the summer.

There is a new grant available to repair traditional farm buildings in the National Park, so I put in Low Park Farm as a potential site. A lady came out from the Yorkshire Dales National Park buildings department and took a lot of photographs. Later in the year we will hear if they considered it was worth putting in an application to renovate the barns. We also have the opportunity to make money for permissions – whether it is Network Rail, Electricity North West or the managers of the ethylene pipeline that need access in order to do work. In the first two months of living here we had payments from Network Rail and Electricity North West, and a booking for an event to use as one of the fields as a car park. The Lunesdale Archaeological Trust had also put in a bid to hold an archaeological dig in the summer, and would pay us for car parking and use one of the buildings to wash and display finds.

My parents had been very busy cleaning out one of the buildings for them to use, and painting noticeboards. Part of our way of providing 'natural capital' can be to engage with the public in events and projects such as this. Another way is to write about farming events in my column in *Cumbria* magazine.

The main way in which we engage directly with the public on a face-to-face basis rather than through social media each year is Open Farm Sunday. The day we took possession of the farm I went onto the Open Farm Sunday website and registered an event. There was an awful lot of tidying up to do, and this would be a good impetus to make us do it, but the main reason that we do Open Farm Sunday is to engage directly with the public and tell our story. Hopefully you have a captive audience, ready to listen to what you consider important about your business. It is also a good opportunity to sell meat directly to the public, so in the run up to Open Farm Sunday I sent five of last year's lambs to the local abattoir to be boxed up for sale.

There was certainly a lot of preparation to do for Open Farm Sunday. Everywhere had to be be tidy and I had to work out what were the key points that I wanted to stress, and how best to do it. I decided that I wanted to talk about the hefted flocks of hill sheep, and the best way of engaging with the public would be to have a sheep X factor. In order to do this I needed to have excellent examples of local sheep, so I invited local breeders of Herdwick, Rough Fell and Swaledale sheep to bring some of their beauty queens to compete in the X Factor.

In order to have the visiting sheep I needed to register a sheep show with the Animal and Plant Health Agency, and get a special holding number from the Department of the Environment Food and Rural Affairs that allowed sheep to come and go on the day without the usual standstill. A vet from the Animal and Plant Health Agency visited to talk to me about bio security, and I also needed to insure the event and have a qualified first aider, hand washing and vehicular disinfecting points etc., so there was quite a lot to do.

I invited the Lunesdale Archaeological Trust, Westmorland Red Squirrels and my friend who is a photographer to have a stall on the day. I also put out some old artefacts from the farm to act as talking points; a clipping stool, bracken sledge and pram. It was quite an undertaking to get all this ready for the big day. There were to be two farm walks at 11am and 2pm, and they were to be free.

In the week before Open Farm Sunday there were a se-

ries of good news/bad news events. The bad news was that none of the sheep breeders that I invited to come for the sheep X factor, for a variety of reasons, were able to come. The other bad news was that we received notification from the Yorkshire Dales National Park that they did not think that it was worth applying for the buildings renovation grant for Low Park Farm, having studied the photographs.

The good news was that the Lunesdale Archaeological Trust had secured funding to do an archaeological dig here in the valley in the summer. They wanted to use one of our buildings to wash and display finds, and use our farm for car parking. It would generate income for the farm, and Dad had now finished clearing out the building for them to use. I painted the existing notice boards that were on the walls to make it a nicer environment for the archaeologists, and then painted some of the walls as well.

I had asked people to book in advance for the farm walks, and after several changes of mind we had seventeen people booked on each walk. The weather was set fair, the farm was tidy, the animals were looking good and I had practiced the farm walk several times. On the Saturday afternoon before the open day my son decided that he would do a refreshment stall, so we got out our large tea urn and went to buy supplies for his stall. He had his cups set up into two piles. If he could sell all the cups in the first pile he would have broken even, if he sold any from the second pile he would have made a profit. I really hoped he did.

The day dawned hot and bright, and I was outside at 6am doing all my usual animal jobs including walking my eight dogs, before the visitors arrived. I had asked the stall-holders to arrive at 10.30 for an 11.00 start, so I was very

surprised when a car pulled into the yard at 9 a.m. It was a couple from Cheshire who had come early in case of any delays on the motorway! They went for a walk and I quickly finished off my jobs. At 10.30 the stallholders arrived, and so by 11.00 we were ready and waiting to be off.

There were 25 people on the first walk. I introduced myself and the first aider (we had to have a first aider and my friend's husband had very kindly volunteered to do this), and then we set off for a tour of the Roman fort. I don't think I had met any of the visitors previously, I assumed they were followers of the Twitter account, and the walk went well. After the walk around the fort we looked at some of the hay meadows, animals including the Dexter cattle, old farmyard and new farm buildings. We ended the walk in the lambing shed. On an old roll of wallpaper I had drawn a diagram of the three-tier sheep system in the UK, and I talked the visitors through why the hill flocks are essential to food production in the UK. I ended the talk by showing a diagram explaining that my lambs had cost £27 each to produce, and in 2016 my best pen of lambs had sold for – you guessed – £27! You could have heard a pin drop. I certainly sold more lamb and mutton than I had expected. Everybody was supportive of my aims for the farm, and the only slightly odd question I had been asked was how much I paid for the farm.

We all went into the farm kitchen for lunch, along with the stallholders. While we were eating one of the visitors popped his head around the kitchen door to say goodbye and insisted on giving me a £10 tip for the walk. It was going well, and cars were already arriving outside for the afternoon walk. I also spotted two local farmers who had arrived and were chatting in the yard. I was looking forward to the afternoon walk as I had several 'friends' that I had chatted to on Twitter and Instagram coming.

By 2pm the farmyard was full of people. I'm not sure exactly how many came on the walk, I think it was about 35. The walk went well again, and we finished off by talking through the stratified sheep system and why the mountain flocks are essential, and why I believe we need to receive a subsidy. Again everybody's attention was held, including the two local farmers who seemed to be as absorbed in the diagram and my explanations as everybody else. I thanked everyone for coming and invited them over to the stallholders to look at the stands. One of the visitors was a baker, and had brought some focaccia bread to share. It was a lovely end to a very successful day. Fergus had made £40 profit on his refreshment stall. His first words to me were, "When are you doing the next one? We can make money out of this."

More important than money, we were building links with consumers, people who would hopefully come back and buy our beef and lamb having seen our farm and our animals. We had 'natural capital', and the ability to show it off. Somehow we needed to turn that into actual capital and build a successful business. It was a good start.

July 2018

"Fair parched everything is," said the farmer's wife. "No rain for weeks and none coming, and no water in the becks. Folks are at their wits' ends in some parts to keep their beasts alive."
Arthur Ransome, *Pigeon Post,* (1936)

I know *Pigeon Post* is a work of fiction, but had I not lived through the summer of 1976 and seen the dry becks of the Lake District for myself, I would have said it was totally unrealistic. In the last 25 years that I had lived in Cumbria we had never seen a summer like that. Summers recently had been relentlessly wet. It had been a struggle to make any hay or silage. The usual pattern that we had come to expect was a couple of weeks of dry weather in May, followed by a very wet June, July and August, then a couple of dry weeks in September.

2018 will be remembered not only as the year that we moved to Low Borrowbridge, but also for its extremes of weather. After the snow at the end of March, which was worse than any I had seen in my life, we were now bizarrely living through the hottest, driest summer in living memory.

When we bought the farm we were very pleased that there were no major issues with the boundaries. On one side the farm is bordered by the main West Coast railway

line, and on the other by the River Lune. We have about three and a half miles of riverbank that forms the boundary of our fields on the east side. We kept a close eye on sheep going too near the riverbank at lambing time, but did not expect that by mid-May the river would be virtually empty of water, leaving all our boundaries open to the Howgill fells and the common land there.

The first problem that we had was our Dexter cattle walking across the river and onto the common, so we bought some electric fencing to contain them. Unfortunately it would be a very expensive job to fence all the riverbank, so we only fenced the bits where the cows were. We then had problems with sheep coming off the common onto our land, and then cattle from neighbouring farms walking across and settling themselves down at Low Park Farm. We moved our cows out of Low Park, but they then somehow escaped and were relaxing enjoying the sun on the common. It was a constant battle to keep track of where everything was.

Long term we intended to plant trees all along the riverbank and fence them off as riparian strips, but in the short term we just had to manage as best we could.

A positive to the hot dry weather was that it was very easy to make hay and haylage. The meadows around Low Borrowbridge had been shut up after lambing time, and by mid-June had a good crop of grass on them. The weather apps on our phones were full of sunshine, so we cut and baled for haylage and hay. We made 118 big bales of haylage on the first cut at Low Borrowbridge, and about 400 small bales of hay. A local farmer with a collection of vintage machinery came to make the small bales, and I raked in the edges of the grass.

It was a timeless scene, the vintage tractor and baler working away and me raking the grass in a summer dress. In the evening I drove our own tractor while the boys loaded the bales onto the bale trailer, and we all stacked the hay barn to the rafters. We wondered how many years it was since the old barn had been full of hay, as the previous owners had made big bales of silage. It was unknown, as was such a lot about our new farm, but we had a big pile of wrapped haylage bales, and a barn full of hay. That would give us a head start on whatever the winter threw at us.

One of the fields at Low Park Farm was also cut for hay. We kept 200 bales of hay for ourselves as an emergency back up, and sold the rest straight off the field to a dairy farmer who was struggling for grass to feed his cows due to the lack of rainfall. It really was a topsy-turvy year. Three months ago we couldn't even access our fields due to the snow, and now we had a sizzling summer and an abundance of hay.

It's a very emotional business making hay, not only because the farm will rely upon the hay for fodder in the winter. Somehow you feel very connected to everyone who has come before you making hay on those meadows, and filling the barns with hay. Since the advent of silage making hot, dry weather has become less critical for the farm's survival, thank goodness, but years ago the very existence of the farm for another year would have been dependant on getting another crop of hay. The happiness that we feel when making small bales of hay, and the enjoyment in stacking them in the hot, dusty barn, never grumbling about the hard, scratchy labour, connects us directly to those who have worked the farm before. We all feel as if we have done a great week's work and achieved a lot. You just don't get the same feeling of satisfaction from looking at a pile of silage bales wrapped in plastic.

A contractor can come into your fields and two men can bale, wrap and stack your silage bales for you in an afternoon, but it takes a whole family or community to make hay. Whatever else you planned to do must be suspended and everyone must work together to get the hay in. A lot of jobs in farming have lost their community feeling due to mechanisation, often just one person is working alone in a tractor, but it has to be all hands on deck to make small bales of hay. The feeling of satisfaction at working together towards a joint purpose is palpable. Small bales are great for foddering too as they are easier to handle, carry and get to out of the way places.

Another issue that the hot dry weather was bringing was wildfires. Again it is a preoccupation in *Pigeon Post* with Mrs Tyson saying: "They've had fires and enough on yon side of the lake, where they've plenty of folk to put them out. But here, with none to help us, we'll be burnt like a handful of tow."

When I lived in the Lake District and we were having a discussion about stocking rates of cattle and sheep on the common where I had my fell rights at a commoners meeting, one of the older farmers commented: "What everyone forgets is that if we reduce numbers on the common any more and we get a hot summer the whole lot will go up like a tinder box." Natural England were suggesting that the numbers of grazing animals on the common were reduced as part of an environmental stewardship agreement, and the more experienced farmers had a real concern about wildfires taking hold in hot weather due to an abundance of dry vegetation.

It turned out that concern was justified, day after day on the news there were more reported wildfires, with people living near commons having to be evacuated from their homes in Lancashire. Several of these fires were in areas that had been fenced off to exclude grazing livestock while trees were planted. It appeared as if the rewilding was fuelling the wildfires. There is no substitute for experience, and it is a constant frustration to many farmers that those who administer environmental schemes do not value their long experience, in some cases going back generations.

Many of our neighbours at Low Borrowbridge considered the fells around us to be undergrazed, and in a poor condition ('going to pot'). This was because sheep had been excluded in many areas in favour of cattle, and new trees had been planted with fencing around to exclude grazing livestock. This was by the new owners and tenants on the other lots of our farm that had been sold at the auction, and an environmental agreement that the commoners had entered into. There was now a lot of gazing upwards to the fells, discussing the excess vegetation and a real fear that we would experience a wildfire. If this happened it would be catastrophic for biodiversity, as plants and wild animals would be lost to the fire.

Pigeon Post again: "And then once more, when it had almost seemed that the fire was sweeping past them, the wind wavered, a line of fire raced across the ground under the smoke, and the sea of bracken, in which so often the scouts had lurked, flared up with a crackling roar as if someone was wasting thousands of fireworks by lighting them all at once."

Haymaking and wildfires aside, the other main job in the summer months is shearing the sheep, or 'clipping' as we call it. This does not harm the sheep, it is just a haircut, and it is essential that it is done in hot weather for welfare issues. Not only could the sheep overheat, but they could also have flies laying their eggs in the long fleeces and become infested with maggots. We regularly treat our sheep with a pour on solution that is meant to prevent this 'fly-strike' and ticks, but sometimes the solution does not work. We had a few instances of sheep and lambs with maggots in their feet this year, and this was due to the fact that we had too much grass. The long grass was giving the sheep 'scald' between their 'toes'. And this in turn sometimes became infested with maggots. It is a horrible condition, but thankfully another application of the pour on solution can get rid of them.

I began shearing the Ouessant sheep myself with hand shears, one each day at feeding time. The fleeces of the rare breed sheep needed to be sheared with the hand shears as they were going to be sold to hand spinners, and it is important that they do not have any 'second cuts' in the fleece, short bits of wool where the shears have gone over the sheep for a second time to tidy them up.

It was very hot work shearing the sheep by hand, but I enjoyed it. It made life easier and more comfortable for the sheep, and I had a saleable product at the end that people can use to make wonderful things. Some of the Ouessant fleeces were sold to a felt artist, and I'm looking forward to seeing the pictures that she produces with them.

In the midst of shearing and haymaking, the Yorkshire Dales National Park sent a botanist to work here for the day to look at the number of priority species of grasses, plants and trees. Three areas were circled on the map that she brought, one is a fenced off area of rush pasture that I had been told was fenced off 'for wildlife', and the other two are woodland areas.

I was very intrigued to see what was in these areas, so I asked if I could accompany her for the morning. Our first stop was the fenced off rush pasture. I had never been in this area before and was keen to understand why it has been fenced off. The botanist explained that she was going to do ten sample areas of two square meters to look at the plants living there, but then all plans were put on hold as she spotted a rare butterfly. It was a small pearl edged fritillary, and the botanist was clearly very excited to see it here. We got some good photos of it, and she said that she would call a

butterfly expert and ask him to come over soon. We quickly Googled the butterfly, and found out that it liked violets. Eight out of ten of her sample areas contained wood violets, so we assumed that is why the area had been fenced off.

We watched quietly and two more of the same butterflies appeared, as well as an abundance of others. This was a really exciting find, but that was not the only thing in this area. There was also a very dried up pond area, with sphagnum moss nearby. In addition there was an abundance of rare and interesting plants and grasses, such as orchids and marsh cinquefoil.

It was an amazing start to the survey, and I drove the botanist on the quad bike to the woodland areas. In these she found some very rare ancient wych elm trees. These are a really special find as they had survived Dutch elm disease in the 1960s and 1970s that destroyed most of the UK's elm trees. I found it very interesting that the trees had been resistant to Dutch elm disease. In a way this validated the work that I had done the previous summer collecting seeds for the Kew Gardens Millennium seedbank.

I collected thousands of seeds from several local trees in a cluster for Kew, organised by Cumbria Wildlife Trust, as trees apparently modify according to their environments and have a local 'type'. These local variations can be disease resistant, and the idea was that if Kew had a store of seeds from around the UK, some of them might be resistant to future catastrophic diseases such as Ash Dieback or Dutch elm disease. Our wych elm trees were living proof of this theory.

The conclusion of the botanist was that there were things here on the farm that merited further investigation, and a full botanical survey of the area. She was going to request that the national park instigated this, and hopefully return to do it. What an exciting day of discovery.

Thankfully towards the end of July we had two days of rain. We desperately needed rain to refill the river and secure our boundary, and help the grass to grow so that we could get a second cut of grass. After the rain the grass visibly grew. Other areas were not so lucky, and much of the UK was now in a serious drought situation.

I continued to investigate diversification ideas. We visited a farm that milks sheep and makes cheese, but we were unable to see the sheep being milked which was a disappointment. It seemed as if the holiday cottage would be an excellent reliable source of income, and I had experience running two holiday cottages previously.

As we live largely in the kitchen to the rear of the farmhouse, we began to wonder if we could make the main house into two holiday cottages, and live in the rear of the house, the original farmhouse. This would generate a good income, but there would be a lot of work to do to get the cottages up to a reasonable standard.

In preparation for renovating the cottages I began buying furniture and other items from my local auction at Penrith and online. The make of furniture that I like, Titchmarsh and Goodwin reproduction Georgian furniture, was very cheap as dark oak furniture is very undesirable at the moment. We saw some for sale in Stockport and hired a van for the day to go down and get it. I bought other bits of furniture from the auction and brought them home in the back of the Land Rover.

There was a lot to look forward to as we sweltered

through the long hot summer. One disappointment was that I received an email to say that the archaeological society would not be using our farm as a base/parking for their archaeological dig as they had found somewhere else to do it. I'm not really sure why they had decided to look elsewhere, it could be because I said that they would have to provide portaloos and not use the house toilets. Whatever the reason it was a loss of potential income and also a lot of work done by Dad in vain, as he had been busy cleaning out a building for them to use. Making a living from a hill farm is not always straightforward. There are so many ideas and income streams to juggle. I just hoped that I could make a success of it.

August 2018

As the days got hotter and hotter, we were also getting nearer and nearer to the autumn sales. It was time to evaluate the farm as best we could having lived here for three months, and decide what stock the farm should carry over our first winter here.

Hector was keen to build up his beef herd, which in time would replace my Dexter herd with more profitable, larger cows. The Dexters are quite hard to manage compared to other cows, they are very wilful, and the amount of meat that they produce is obviously a lot less than a larger cow. He wanted to build up his herd by buying heifers from a farm that he works at in the Howgill fells, as the cows there are very placid and have excellent growth rates and fertility. In an upland area the longevity of some of the cows is remarkable, having produced sixteen calves whilst living out on the fell.

He had the opportunity to buy five Aberdeen Angus heifers from this herd, which he did, and they arrived at Low Borrowbridge and settled in well. This was a significant financial investment for him, and he was really pleased when he was given a Rough Fell tup that he had admired as 'luck'.

He felt that he needed a couple more heifers, and had two in mind at the dairy farm that he works at. These were Stabiliser beef cattle out of a dairy cow. There was one that was red and white striped, like a tiger, that he liked and we went together to choose another. The owner of the cows was an hour late to meet us because he was having a drama with a sheep stuck in sinking sand and we had plenty of time to look at the cows. It was so hot that we lay in the field, with the cows sniffing around us. They were definitely peaceful, placid cows, which was important if I was to be in sole charge of them for several days a week.

We brought the heifers home, and our herd for the winter was confirmed as my six Dexters, the five Aberdeen Angus heifers and the two Stabiliser heifers. Stabiliser are a new, improved breed of beef cattle that have been developed recently to meet market demands for a beef cow.

The sheep flock needed more careful thought. In order to assess what we had and make decisions for the following year we decided to wait until we had all the main flock in for shearing so that we could have a good look at them.

Thankfully no sooner had the archaeologists said that they didn't want to come here, than Network Rail contacted us again with more access requirements. They wanted to send four wallers here for at least four weeks to rebuild walls alongside the railway line, and would like to use our land for parking, siting their 'welfare cabin' and storing their excavator and dumper truck. It's a funny way to make a living, negotiating access onto our land, but it is also a good source of income and is not to be sneezed at.

I also looked again at the Countryside Stewardship scheme and decided that in addition to putting Low Park Farm into a higher level stewardship scheme I would also try and put Low Borrowbridge into a mid-tier scheme this year. I needed to get a move on as the application pack had to be in by the end of August, and I needed to consult the Yorkshire Dales National Park, the Lune Rivers Trust, English Heritage and the Environment Agency amongst other people before deciding which options to pick.

The farmyard would fit well into a historic buildings preservation option. Buildings that were built before 1940 can go into this scheme, and our 'house yard' was certainly built before then. It would be a useful way to pay for repairs to drainpipes and doors if we could get into the scheme. There was also a provision for providing an owl box.

When we first bought Low Borrowbridge there were owls nesting in the old hay barn. Us arriving seemed to frighten them off, and they went down to the old farmhouse at Low Park Farm. Now in mid-summer they had returned and laid their eggs in the roof of the farmhouse at Low Borrowbridge, and were bringing their chicks up here. They accessed the roof through a vent in the chimneystack, and if you went out at dusk not only could you hear the babies crying for their mother's return from hunting, but you could also see their little faces lined up looking out. It was just like a scene from *Owl Babies* by Martin Waddell that I used to read over and over to my children as a bedtime story.

It is very important to me to provide homes for breeding wildlife as well as breeding farm animals. I see the two as equally important. It gives me just as much pleasure to see the owl babies, waiting patiently, as a newborn calf snuggled in the rushes out of the wind. I am not alone in this love of wildlife, and I think this is much misunderstood by the media and some of the public's perception of farmers as cash loving, subsidy guzzling polluters of the land. On the contrary many of us are living on a small amount of money caring for our land and its biodiversity as best we can.

The other options that I considered in the countryside stewardship schemes included repairing walls, laying hedges and creating riparian strips along the river Lune. These would be part of a mosaic of wildlife habitats throughout the farm, and would be areas next to the river where livestock is excluded. Some of these areas have trees planted already, at Low Borrowbridge, other land down to Low Park Farm will require tree planting along about two and a half miles of riverbank. It is a big, ambitious project, but it would aid water quality, flood alleviation and provide habitats for wildlife, so I hope it gets the go ahead. English Heritage, the Environment Agency and the Lune Rivers Trust are all in support of the scheme that would see the livestock excluded from the river and ram pumps used to pump drinking water up to troughs in the fields instead. The location of the troughs has to be carefully chosen in conjunction with English Heritage because the fields are classified as Scheduled Ancient Monuments.

I had to produce a Farm Environment Record for the farm, and a map with the options on. There was quite a lot of work to be done to get the application in, so I hoped it would be successful. It felt like the right thing to be doing, and the other agencies involved seem to agree with me. It took several days work and a couple of late nights filling in forms and interpreting the huge spread sheets that arrived by email detailing our Historic Farm Record, but by the end of August I had an envelope stuffed with forms, maps and letters of support that was posted off to Natural England. All I could do now was wait and hope that our application was successful.

2018 really is the year for expecting the unexpected. It is only to be expected that the unexpected weather conditions would have an effect on the animals' ability to breed this year. Whilst driving out of the farmyard at midnight one night in late summer I looked across to the Ouessant field and thought that the moonlight was playing tricks with me. Lying next to a wall was a sheep that had not had a lamb, and next to her was a small white shape illuminated in the moonlight. I reversed back and had another look, and chuckled to myself that I must be seeing things, the moonlight was making one of the stones at the bottom of the wall look so white that I thought it was a tiny lamb.

The next morning I cursed myself for not having got out of the car to check, as a tiny but thankfully healthy Ouessant lamb came across the field with her mum to see me.

Two things could have happened. The ewe was one of a group of four sheep that were with a younger, unproven tup and only one of them had lambed. It could be that this tup had a problem such as a virus, and had not been fertile enough to get the others pregnant, or it could be that these young sheep were pregnant but had lost their lambs in the whole 'beast from the east' and moving farm experience. Either way I now expected the other two sheep to lamb and kept an hourly watch on them out of the kitchen window or over the wall. By the following morning both had healthy lambs, and we had three unseasonably late but happy, playful lambs.

There were two main big jobs to do in August, clipping (shearing the sheep) and weaning. There were also meat boxes to be produced and posted out from last year's lambs, now fattened for fifteen months on our species rich grassland. The first big job was clipping.

After all the warm weather we had come to expect hot, dry weather, so it was a bit of a shock when our first, then our second attempt at clipping was rained off. We wanted to clip the sheep at the weekend when there would be plenty of people around to help gather the sheep. The first weekend we looked out of the bedroom windows at 5am and went back to bed.

The second weekend we got out of bed at 5am, had breakfast and were heading down the valley by 5.30am. We got about two miles from home and it started to rain, so we turned back. On the third weekend my son and husband had gone to look at a tractor near Blackpool first thing in the morning, so we didn't get started on our gather until about 10am, but it all went according to plan.

Ideally we need four people to gather the sheep. The land is a long strip, so we drive down to the bottom and start from there. We gather all the sheep along the strip as we go. It is about three and a half miles long. We drive there on the quad and in the Land Rover as we may need both vehicles.

I walked in front of the sheep calling them for the whole length of the gather. As soon as the older sheep hear me calling, they run over and follow, and their lambs follow them. They associate me with food, having been fed through winter, and are very happy to follow me on the off chance that they may get food. I shout 'come on girls, come on girls' and if the sheep are out of sight and hear they will come.

I walk with the sheep jostling behind me. My husband

Antony and son Hector take the sides of the land, Antony running on foot and Hector on the quad. All the sheep who do not see or hear me, or chose to ignore me, must be guided along in the right direction. It is very important to stay just a little way behind them and anticipate their movements, moving quickly to the left or right to make them move in the opposite direction and make them follow me. Antony and Hector have to work hard, darting about and making sure that everybody is heading in the right direction.

My youngest son Fergus drives at the back of all the sheep, bringing up the rear in the Land Rover. If any sheep looks ill or is struggling to walk he may have to put them in the back of the Land Rover, but usually everyone is alright. Sometimes a sheep can get an eye infection that renders them temporarily blind, and of course it is very hard for them to keep going in the right direction then. This is usually caused by the wind in winter and we call it 'wind blindness'.

About half way along the land there is a dividing gate. Thankfully we had left this gate closed as by the time we got to the gate on clipping day we had also gathered all the cows with us, and we did not want them to come in. Hector used his knowledge of animal psychology and shouted: "Just keep walking towards the gate with them all. The cows are cleverer than the sheep. They will see the gate is closed and turn back first."

He was right, but it is a bit of a squash with all of the sheep and cows and us on a narrow track heading towards a gateway. I advised Antony not to make eye contact with the bull, who was looming over him, and thankfully Eric the bull decided to turn back as well.

Once all the cows had turned back I went to open the gate, and at this point the sheep decided that they too wanted to turn back. Thankfully we had three people and two vehicles positioned behind them and they decided to carry on.

Beyond the gate there is a track with fencing on either side that I can lead the sheep down on my own, while everybody else moves sheep in the fields to the left and right of the track. We were all heading in the same direction, and met up at the bottom of a big hill. The tups were there in a field and were waiting at the gate, keen to join all the ladies in the chaotic scene. Not today boys, you will have to wait until November to be back amongst the girls.

Before long I could see Hector and Antony approaching with streams of sheep in front of them. We all met at the gate at the bottom of the hill, and all that remained now was to walk the sheep about a mile alongside the River Lune, and gather them in a pen before walking them the last half mile along the road to the farm. Everyone was in a buoyant mood as the gather had been relatively easy, and the sheep were moving along quite happily. Nobody had needed a ride, Fergus was bringing up the rear in the Land Rover without any casualties on board.

Along the last 300m of riverbank before the road there are two gates that can be closed, moving the sheep into a smaller and smaller pen. They were now gathered into the pen, and I phoned home to ask my parents to come out of the house and stop any traffic going down the road. They also had to do the crucial job of making sure the sheep turned into the farmyard and did not head straight along the

road towards Kendal. Very luckily the postman happened to be there in his van at this time, so he could be roped in to help block the road as well.

The idea was that I would lead the sheep up the road, whilst everybody else drove through the fields to get home and into the farmyard ready to pen the sheep there. As soon as I opened the gates there was an almighty rush, and I found that I was following the sheep down the road and not leading them – on my own. I frantically phoned home to check that Mum and Dad had come out of the house already, but there was no answer, which was a good thing.

Thankfully it all ran like clockwork, the sheep moved at a reasonable pace along the road, and turned into the yard. We were then able to direct them all into the cow shed. From the cow shed there is a small lean to, and we then squashed all the sheep into there. It is much easier to work with sheep if they do not have a large area to run about in and evade capture, it makes the whole experience less stressful for them and the farmers.

Some hurdles were then brought in to divide the lean to into two. We sorted them into lambs and sheep. Hector would be shearing all the sheep and I would be giving the lambs their booster injection for a variety of sheep diseases, marking them with a red line to show that they belonged to us, and giving them a bolus and a dose of wormer. The bolus is a slow release of cobalt, selenium and iodine that will help the lambs to grow. It is administered with a 'gun' that slides the bolus down their throat and into their rumen. It is a careful job to be undertaken as the gun can scratch their throat if applied at the wrong angle.

So, I made myself busy with the lambs. I pulled the

hurdles across and made a small pen then they were easy for Fergus to send one out of for me, and set up a footbath for them to walk through on their way out after having the treatments. They could walk out and into the cow shed where they would be happily reunited with their mothers. The footbath should stop them getting any foot problems during the summer months.

Hector had all of the sheep in his section of the lean to, and set about shearing them steadily and methodically with the sheep shearing machine hanging from the roof of the shed. After they had been sheared he marked them red, and put them through the footbath and into the cow shed. The fleeces were passed to my parents who had to follow my confusing instructions:

- Rare breed fleeces to be 'skirted' (any muck taken off) and rolled with the wool tucked inside and put into card-board boxes to send to the spinning mill.
- Herdwick fleeces to be rolled with the fleece on the in-side. Any complete fleeces to be put in a cardboard box for felt artists, and any incomplete into the wool bag.
- Rough Fell fleeces to be rolled with the fleece on the outside and put into the wool bag.
- Any other fleeces to be rolled with the fleeces on the in-side and put into the wool bag.

Putting fleeces into the wool bag is an admission that they are virtually worthless, as we will receive on average about 30p for them.

We all worked slowly and steadily at our jobs, with tea breaks in the morning and afternoon and a lunch break. By the evening all the sheep had been sheared, and all the lambs dosed. They had all had plenty of time to find their lambs in the cow shed, and were ready to go back outside. The road needed to be blocked by the river this time, to prevent the sheep from running down the lane towards the Howgill Fells. Antony blocked the road with the Land Rover parked sideways across it, and we let the sheep out of the cow shed. They ran straight out of the yard and down the lane, with me following them on foot and Hector on the quad. A family of holidaymakers then arrived in a car behind us, and the children's faces were a picture as they stuck their heads out of the windows to see all the sheep and lambs walking along the road.

I was very happy to see them set off along the river and turn back and get into a nice hot bath. Antony was going for a run along the river, and as soon as I got out of the bath he arrived back saying that I had to get dressed quickly as he had found a sheep that we had missed, and it had maggots in one of its feet. So, old clothes went back on, and off I went on the quad again to find the sheep, bring it home on the quad and get rid of the maggots. I was very glad to get into bed that night.

The next morning, Sunday, we were up and out again early looking for sheep that we had missed. There were bound to be sheep that had not heard the gather, or had hidden somewhere so we did not see them. This time we pushed them in front of us, and down towards the sheep pens at Low Park Farm. There were five sheep and their lambs. Two of the sheep were not ours, so three sheep missed was not a bad result at all. Hector hung his shearing machine from an oak tree above the pen, and he sheared the three sheep while I sorted the lambs. The visiting sheep

were identified by their ear tags, and put into the quad trailer and returned.

It had been a very productive weekend. The sheep would feel much better in the humid weather without their fleeces on, and there would be much less chance of them getting infested with maggots without their long woolly coats. Like the haymaking, it had been another team effort and it was very satisfying to get the job done without any hitches or arguments. There were still other jobs to do in August, but this was the main one that needed to be completed. Now I just needed to sort out sending the wool off to the right people, and then we could concentrate on the next big job, weaning the lambs.

Unchanging Patterns

"To house, and feed by hand my weaning lambs,
And drain the strutting udders of their dams?"
Virgil's Pastorals (c42-37BC)

Nothing much changes in sheep farming and shepherding. Between 42 and 37 years BC, around a hundred years before the first Roman soldiers built a fortification at Low Borrowbridge, the Roman poet Virgil was writing about the decision to wean his lambs in a series of pastoral poems. This preoccupation is still with us two thousand years later.

Even more remarkably, he writes two poems (the first and ninth) lamenting the expulsion of shepherds from their family farms for political reasons, and the loss of his own family farm after the Battle of Philippi in 42BC. The media in 2018 are busy discussing the same issue, what will happen if hill farmers are out of business and have to leave their family farms after the political upheaval of the UK leaving the European Union? The phrase 'Virgilian' came to mean the sorrow expressed by those dispossessed of farms and livelihoods. We have to hope that there are not too many farmers displaying Virgilian sorrow after the new political landscape decides on how to subsidise farming in the uplands, or not, as the case may be.

When to wean the lambs is a crucial decision that is usually based upon a gut reaction that the time is right, as well as lamb growth rates, grass growth rates and ewe condition. Our main concern this year was ewe condition, as our lambs were remarkably growing better than ever before, despite the extreme weather, and we had plenty of grass as our farm was under stocked and the period of drought seemed to be over in Cumbria if not in the rest of the country.

The ewes were looking tired and thin after shearing, and we decided to wean the lambs on 11 August, which is around twelve weeks after the majority of the lambs were born. We needed time for the ewes that we were keeping for another year to regain their body condition before they meet the tup again in November. Hill ewes are traditionally separated from their lambs at this time before the grass in the uplands begins to lose its nutritional quality in the autumn. They cannot be put onto rich grass straight away at weaning, as they need a good two weeks to 'dry off' and stop producing milk. Lambs, in contrast, require good quality grass to make up for the nutritional value of the loss of their mother's milk.

So, on 11 August the four of us set off again on a Saturday morning to gather the sheep. An added complication to the gather this time was that something had broken on the quad bike. It would only go in 4-wheel drive, not 2-wheel drive, and only two of the four wheels were turning. This was very tricky to drive, if you wanted to go uphill you had to reverse!

Thankfully the sheep were very compliant and Hector did not have to do too many death-defying manoeuvres on the quad bike. It was another beautifully sunny day as we walked the sheep along the River Lune, down the lane and into the farm yard. They ran into the cow shed again, and we put them through the footbath and into the little lean to.

The lambs and the ewes were then separated. The lambs were put outside into a very lush field, part of which had been separated off for them with electric fencing; the remainder was hopefully going to be cut for silage. The lambs moved very sensibly out into the field, which is not always the case when they do not have their mothers with them, and began eating the lush green grass.

The male hoggs that had been fattened for fifteen months on grass and were almost ready to go to the butchers to make meat boxes also went into this field. The ewes were checked for lameness, and their feet trimmed and treated if necessary, before they were walked back down to the rough grazing that they had just come from with their lambs.

Instead of a cacophony of noise coming along the road, it was silent. The ewes quietly walked away from their lambs, they knew the routine having done this several times before. I wondered if they wondered whether their lambs were being kept for breeding, and whether they would meet their daughters again in the New Year. Probably not, I think to be honest they were generally relieved to get some peace and quiet and freedom from the constant responsibility of looking after lambs. They were now on holiday until November. The lambs were weaned; we could now turn our attention to some retail therapy.

We set off the next morning for County Durham with our large sheep trailer ready for our purchases. Some Herdwick breeders that we follow on Twitter were reducing their flock. The good thing about buying from someone that you follow on social media is that you can get some idea of the care that the sheep have had. We had seen them regularly going through the footbath, and taking pride in their flock by making expensive purchases at auction and doing well at shows.

We would be buying their older sheep, ones that were still 'correct below' (two functioning udders) and 'full mouthed' (had all their teeth). There were 21 sheep available, and we were very happy to take them. They also gave us a nice gimmer lamb 'for luck', and before the afternoon was out they were happily grazing along the banks of the River Lune. We hoped they would stay there. We needed to buy about another 200 sheep.

Our other big purchase before the winter was the tractor that Antony and Hector had gone to Blackpool to see. We needed a four wheel drive tractor that could negotiate snow on hills, for when we found ourselves in severe weather situations again. They bought a Massey Ferguson 390T.

It had been registered 23 years ago, so it was not a 'new' tractor but it was new to us and a significant improvement on our other machinery. We would now be able to save money by being able to do more jobs ourselves without calling in contractors. Hector also bought a front and rear 'bale cuddler' to move about the big bales of silage that we had made.

There were a few other things that we still needed to buy, such as some cattle ring feeders and a quad bike trailer. The one we were using was borrowed. There were also running repairs to do; the bearings on the wheels of the small sheep trailer collapsed, the Land Rover doors would not stay shut and needed replacing, the tin sheeting blew off

the sheep shed in a storm, a tap got left on and the water tank emptied, a friend's working Border collie unexpectedly had ten puppies the day before she went on holiday so the puppies and their mum came for a holiday here. Life was never short of jobs to do or things to buy. We could never complain of being bored.

In mid-August I had an afternoon out at what was now my local show, Ravenstonedale Show. It is a traditional Cumbrian show with a sheep show, dog show, fell race, various craft and produce classes, craft marquee, children's sports and a brass band playing. I took Ruby to enter into the 'small dog other than a terrier' class. Unfortunately she did not win a rosette, as she was too busy fussing about having to have a collar and lead on to stand up smartly and smile at the judge. The rain almost held off, it blew in great swathes of 'mizzle' across the field.

I had on boots, waterproofs, two scarves and a woolly hat. Dogs were not allowed in the marquees so I had to stay outside and was unable to look at the novelty vegetable entries which are always very amusing.

The hoggs and few older sheep, along with the two pigs, went to the abattoir one wild windy night. Hector had been working late and it was almost dark and pouring down with rain as Fergus and I gathered in the sheep and then encouraged the pigs up the ramp. The sheep were on the top deck of the trailer with the pigs underneath.

It was like the middle of winter as we crept along the motorway, hardly able to see out of the windscreen because it was raining so hard. We stopped for petrol in Kendal, and a vicar was keeping the man at the petrol station company. The vicar asked what was in the trailer, and then asked my advice about putting a pig in his vicarage garden to clear it of brambles. It was one of those surreal conversations that you seem to encounter at the most inopportune times. The movement website had been refusing to accept my details, and we were much later than planned setting off, yet here we were chatting to a vicar at the petrol station. I think I convinced him not to get any pigs.

I was not particularly sorry to say goodbye to the pigs as they had been particularly bad tempered, and it had been quite a stressful day. The rain hammered down on my bedroom window and I slept fitfully, dreaming of pigs, abattoirs, vicars and vicarage gardens. It was quite a relief when the alarm went off at 6am and I could get up.

The meat from the sheep and the pigs was sold privately to meat box customers, and I had to confirm their orders, send invoices, buy the meat boxes and freeze the ice packs ready for collecting the meat five days later. It is not the easiest way to sell meat, but it is very rewarding selling meat to people who appreciate the quality of life that the animals have had.

The following night we were again working after dark. It had been the most miserable night and day in terms of weather. Rain had been falling steadily without any let up. The river was gushing along, in spate. One of the cows, the last one to calve this year, had appeared earlier in the day to be close to calving, so Hector went down to check she was all right. She was about two miles from home, and had somehow got under the electric fencing and calved next to the riverbank. The cow and calf were fine, but they had taken a bit of finding in amongst all the vegetation next to the river.

I set off early in the morning to check that the cow and calf were all right. Hector had walked them away from the riverbank the previous night, but they were now under the fence and settled in their spot again. I watched to make sure that the calf was drinking, and then set about looking for the other cows. It soon became apparent that they were not where they should be; in fact they had crept around the edge of the fence right next to the riverbank and were fast approaching Low Borrowbridge, some two miles away from where they should have been.

I did a headcount and discovered that six cows were missing. It was absolutely torrential rain, blowing gusty wind, and I was on the quad bike steering with one hand and holding one hand above my eyes so that I could see through the driving rain. There was no sign of the missing cows, so I drove right to the end of the farm and came back, the full length of the 3.5 mile strip darting around everywhere on the quad. I could feel now that my arms were wet up to the elbows, where rain had blown in down my sleeves, and on my bottom half I was soaked right through to the skin. I must have put on my old, leaky waterproof trousers by mistake.

There was no sign of the cows, so I reached through several layers to get my phone out of my pocket to call Hector. The phone had been on silent, and I hadn't seen that I had a message telling me that six cows had swum across the river and were currently on the opposite riverbank near a neighbour's house.

By the time I drove there he had contained them in a field, as they had looked as if they were going to attempt to swim back across the river and he was worried that they would drown. As it was so wet neither of us felt like walking the cows home, so we agreed to meet again in the evening and walk them home then.

The cows took some finding in the evening, as they had escaped from his field and up into some woodland. It had stopped raining by now but the midges were ferocious as we searched for the cows. After about an hour we managed to get them onto the road, over the packhorse bridge and back down the lane to our land. It was then a slow two-mile walk to take them back to the field that they should have been in. By the time we got there it was pitch black, and for the third consecutive night we were working in the dark. Autumn must be here.

A week after the pigs were taken to the abattoir the meat was collected and sorted out into piles for internet orders. They had been rather an unknown quantity; we just didn't know how much meat we could expect from a pig. I also hadn't realised that the bacon would have to be collected two weeks later than the rest of the meat because it had to be cured.

We ended up with 32 shoulder/leg roasting joints and 40 packs of twelve sausages. This was more than I had orders for, so I put a sign outside the house and managed to sell more meat that way. What an entrepreneur you have to be to be a modern farmer. In one day I sold various quantities of sausages and pork, half hogget and half mutton meat boxes, books, hats and sheep decorations made from Herdwick wool, along with whole fleeces. I was also advertising our upcoming farm open day on Twitter and trying to sell tickets to that at £3 each.

Alongside all of this commercial activity, it was time for the farrier to visit to file and check the ponies' feet. The ponies had never come into the farmyard before, so I was rather nervous about whether they would come in sensibly. Fergus and I went to collect them, and only Bella would have her headcollar and lead on. We had to use our usual strategy of pretending to take Bella on her own, as then the others will follow because they don't want to miss out on what is going on. Apple and Susan followed us right to the road near the farmyard, and then I shut the gate after Bella and told Fergus to keep walking for home. At this point Apple and Susan decided, as they always did, that they would reluctantly let me put their head collars on.

After that it was rather straight forward, and the girls walked very sensibly into the yard and then into the 'little lean to'. I spent a very productive Friday night grooming their manes and tails. Apple spent a happy evening sniffing my hair and putting her huge muzzle right in my face so that it was difficult to see what I was doing with the other ponies' manes. You can't push away love though.

The farrier arrived bright and early the following day.

The girls behaved impeccably, not a spot of bother, and they were soon back out in the fields grazing happily. The farrier does not shoe the ponies, only gives them a trim and a file, and checks that their feet are healthy.

The rest of the afternoon was spent in getting the sheep ready for Kentmere Sheep Show. This is a shepherd's meet in a Lake District valley, and I had been asked to judge the 'Native and Rare Breed sheep' there the previous year. There had only been two farmers entering sheep in these classes, and I had promised to take some of my sheep this year to swell the numbers.

I had hoped to take my Welsh sheep, which were looking washed and blow-dried to perfection after all the wind and the rain that we had had in the last week. As ever, when I try to show sheep, there were several spanners in the works. The first was that Hector had been to a machinery auction and bought two bale cuddlers, to fit on the front and back of the new (old) tractor. This would make feeding the animals in the winter a lot easier. The bale cuddlers had been dropped into the small sheep trailer (with the top removed) at the auction, and the wheel bearings of the trailer had collapsed. Thankfully this had happened at home in the yard and not driving home on the motorway.

The small sheep trailer was therefore out of action, and I had not passed my trailer test to take the large trailer. Nobody wanted to come to the sheep show with me, so I would have to think of an alternative plan. A possible plan was that I could take a couple of Ouessant sheep in the back of the Land Rover. They travel much more safely in the back of the Land Rover, as they are so tiny.

This seemed like a possible plan, apart from the indica-

123

tors on the Land Rover were not working properly. If the Land Rover had been left outside in torrential rain, somehow rain could get into the indicators and stop them from working until they dried out. I parked the Land Rover in the barn and hoped they would dry out in time.

I then asked Hector to come and help me load the sheep I wanted to show into the quad trailer. I successfully caught the Ouessant tup, but then we noticed that the Rough Fell tup was lying down, not moving, in the field at the top of the hill. No amount of whistling could make him stir. I put the Ouessant tup into the trailer and Hector said we would drive up and check the tup was alive.

It was on the tip of my tongue to tell Hector that I didn't think that the courtesy quad bike was very good at pulling a trailer uphill, but the next thing I knew I was being thrown off the back of the quad as the front wheels went up in the air. I was thrown into the front of the quad trailer. The tup decided he didn't like this trailer, who can blame him, and got his front legs out ready to jump out. I quickly grabbed him, while Hector carefully reversed downhill. After waking the Rough Fell tup up from a deep sleep, we drove back to the farmyard at a very sedate speed, while I held onto the tup with one hand and examined the bruises on my arms with the other.

The indicators on the Land Rover dried out overnight and were functioning properly. My only concern now was that the Ouessant tup might try and jump through the rear window of the Land Rover, so I tied the aluminium gates from inside the small sheep trailer inside the back of the Land Rover and filled the cargo area with straw.

The day dawned dry, but by the time we had met and

sold meat to two meat box customers and got ready for the show it was decidedly wet. There were lots of competitors in the 'Native and Rare Breed' class. There was no pre-entry, you simply turned up on the day and paid £1 per sheep to enter. I anxiously calculated how many competitors were going to be in each age group by looking at the sheep, and the statistical probability of going home empty handed.

I need not have worried. My very aggressive tup won his 'aged tup' class, and I had a red rosette and a £5 note in my pocket, everything was going to be OK. When the judge had asked the tups to be let go, so that she could see them walk, mine had taken a flying jump about three foot in the air. He spread his front and back legs out and he looked like he was flying above the sheep pens. Several spectators said "Ooooohhh". Imagine having a sheep that can make people gasp with amazement. Thankfully he did not jump clean out of the pens and down the valley. That would have made me gasp with exasperation.

The other sheep did reasonably well, everyone got a rosette. We got second group of sheep, after drafting in help from a photographer friend and a spectator to hold two of the sheep. The tup went into the championship, but we did not win champion sheep.

After the judging I went and sat in the marquee and had a cheese and pickle sandwich, and a piece of coffee cake and a mug of tea. Life lived to its fullest. After paying 1 pound each for the sheep to enter the show, and buying my lunch out of my prize money, I had made a profit of two pounds. That's what I call a successful day. Who says there is no money in hill farming?

Almost Autumn

August drew to a close, and the 'backend' had set in. It seemed to be always raining a constant drizzle that blew about in the wind. There would hopefully be a good weather window in September to get the second cut of grass.

Driving about I noticed numerous signs for shows and outdoor events. I still hadn't got all my clothes and boots dry from Kentmere Sheep Show, and wondered if in the past August was a drier month if all these outdoor events are scheduled to take place then.

I saw a sign for Crosby Ravensworth Show. It was on the last Thursday in August, and it reminded me of a story that my grandad told me about Crosby Show. When he was driving trains from London to Edinburgh before he retired he was working with a man who had been evacuated to Crosby Ravensworth during the Second World War. My grandad commented that was near where he was from, and asked him did he get back to Crosby often? The man confessed that he had never been back, he had never learnt to drive and there isn't a railway station within walking distance of Crosby. He said that he felt bad as he had told the lady that he stayed with, who hadn't any children of her own, that he would go back and visit.

My grandad said that the next day they both had off together they would go to Crosby Ravensworth and see if she was still alive. It was 33 years since his friend had set foot in the village. They both had the following Thursday off, and had agreed not to take any 'bait' (packed lunch) as Grandad knew that there was a pub in Crosby Ravensworth where they could get a nice dinner.

When they arrived in Crosby the pub door was locked, and there was nobody about except one man hurrying down the street. Grandad asked him why the pub was shut, and if there was anywhere where they could get a hot dinner. The man explained that it was show day. He was rushing home because he had a cow calving, but the sit down lunch in the marquee was just about to start, and he had two complimentary tickets. He told them just to go in and find a spare seat, thrust the lunch tickets into their hands and hurried off.

Grandad and his friend went to the show, and stuck their heads into the marquee door. They were looking around for a spare seat, and the whole marquee went deadly quiet and still as the two strangers stood there, all but for one old lady who struggled to her feet and said "I knew you would come back!"

I was amazed when Grandad told me this story. I asked him was it true, did she instantly recognise the man of 43 who she hadn't seen since he was ten. Grandad insisted that she did, and commented, "It's a good job we didn't take our bait boxes or we might never have found her." My heart goes out to that poor lady, waiting 33 years for her evacuee to go back and visit her. I'm so glad that they did. What a tale.

Another of Grandad's stories concerning marquees in August was when he was driving a train on the Settle to

Carlisle line one Saturday in August. They saw a marquee next to the train line, and he realised it was the wedding of some farming friends that he knew. He said to his fireman "We'll stop on the way back."

In the evening on the way back they stopped the train, full of local people going home after shopping on Saturday afternoon, and they all climbed down the railway embankment and went to wish the bride and groom well, passengers and railway staff alike. They had a cup of tea and a piece of wedding cake, and then they all got on the train again and set off. Can this be true? The trains thundering past Low Borrowbridge today are definitely not stopping for tea and cake.

We have all become train spotters living here. We know the big freight trains and their times, and I look out for the Royal Mail train as it makes a bright red streak through the valley. There is also one Virgin train that is covered in Union Jacks that I like to look out for. I am absolutely amazed at the amount of effort that it takes to maintain the railway, not only in the many projects that request access through our land, but the many men working at night with torches on the line. I can see now why train tickets are so expensive. It must be a huge undertaking to run a company like Network Rail, and I am pleased that they put so much effort into keeping everyone safe.

Grandad had some exciting experiences on the railway line that passes through our farm as well. He was in a 're-served occupation' during the Second World War, meaning that he had to stay here and continue to work on the rail-ways and not join the army. A big part of his job in wartime was moving large groups of soldiers or trains full of provisions and supplies around the country. Trains full of soldiers and supplies were obvious targets for German planes, and they had to keep their wits about them.

Grandad was the fireman on a train full of soldiers trav-elling over Shap summit, and the steam train had to stop at the water troughs to refill. He was refilling the train with his driver, when suddenly a German plane appeared flying straight towards the train. I can well understand how these planes come suddenly from nowhere, as we still get Royal Air Force planes training here flying through the gorge at low levels most afternoons. Grandad and the driver ran for cover, and hid under the water tank. The plane shot at the engine, but missed and hit the water tank. All the water rushed out of the tank onto Grandad and the driver. The train was in danger of exploding as they had no water to refill it and all the soldiers had to evacuate the train, but they were all very lucky to survive. If the bullets had hit the engine and not the water tank none of them would have lived to tell the tale.

The railway is an important part of the history of our farm, there were two railway cottages built next to the line (before it was electrified) from stone recycled from the Roman fort. These cottages were demolished with the coming of the motorway. Previously the railway was a huge employer for the area, today lots of local people work at the motorway services; Tebay North, Tebay South and the Truckstop. These services are run by a family company as a 'farmshop' and are generally considered to be the best motorway services in the UK. The family have opened sister sites in Gloucester and Cairn Lodge.

Throughout all this time, with massive infrastructure projects being developed alongside it, people have lived and worked on our farm, developing and diversifying to try to make a living. That is what I must do, build a business and build a future for our family. When I think of the task ahead I think of a tiny woman stood in the bottom of a huge valley, dwarfed by the landscape around her.

There were plenty of jobs to do at the end of August before we could turn our attention fully to the sheep sales. The lambs needed to have their second vaccination, and the ewes needed to be moved to better grazing now that their milk had dried up. Hector was busy getting the barns ready for winter, repairing cow cubicles and water troughs. I still needed to send the wool off for spinning, and some soil samples to see what condition our fields were in, and ewe blood samples to see how they were for minerals and nutrients.

Moving the ewes to better grazing was relatively straightforward. They were getting used to the layout of the farm now, and the fact that we regularly moved them about. We walked them down to The Allotment, this had been the allotment for Low Park Farm. It was covered in a rich abundance of green grass, the cows had been moved out of there a few weeks before and the grass had grown back beautifully.

The ewes looked very thin, as they always do at this time of year. A ewe that is in good condition at this time of year will not have been feeding her lambs well, unless we have been giving her extra food for any reason. One or two were limping, and we needed to catch them and trim their feet. Otherwise they walked well into the allotment.

They were now officially on holiday until 5 November. By then we wanted them to ideally be 'Body Condition Score' 3. Body condition scoring is a way of assessing and recording how much 'condition' there is on a sheep (how tubby they are). Some of ours were currently about 1.5, some 2. It would take them at least a month to put on a condition score. They had eight weeks in which to put on the right amount of weight to be ready to meet the tup and conceive their lambs. They are fed only on grass.

The lambs were brought into the farmyard and run through the footbath again. Footbathing them seemed to be preventing them from getting 'scald' in between the 'toes' of their feet. Scald can be caused by long grass. The lamb were all vaccinated for a second time, this should protect them from a variety of diseases until March when every sheep on the farm receives their annual booster jab.

Not everything was going well. Bringing my Welsh sheep into the pens every day in preparation for the West-morland Show seemed to be making them tamer, but with less than two weeks to the show my two best lambs, one gimmer and one tup, went down with fly strike. This is when flies lay eggs in the fleeces of sheep and maggots hatch out. By the time I spotted it they had an area the size of a saucer on their back that was infested.

I went inside and told Hector we would have to get the clipping machine out as my two best lambs had fly strike and would have to be clipped. I was very disappointed that this had happened, and he did not make me feel any better by saying that I should have spotted it sooner, and that there was no point in me checking sheep if I was going to miss things like this.

To look on the bright side, I had spotted it early enough to save the lambs. We sheared them and put on a solution that killed the maggots. There was no way that these sheep could be shown this year now. It was a real blow to our plans to show sheep at the Westmorland Show. Without the tup lamb I could not show in the group section that I had entered. I had such high hopes for them, but then if I wasn't a realist I don't think I could be a shepherdess. Bad things happen. You just have to accept them and move on.

September

"Soon to be put to the test
To be whipped by the winds of the West
She carries on through it all
She's a waterfall"
                    Waterfall by The Stone Roses

By the first week of September there was a rather large elephant sitting in the corner of the farm kitchen. That elephant was the fact that we had now run out of money in our farm account. Our incomings for the year, despite my book sales, knitwear orders and meat sales, stood at less than our outgoings, excluding equipment that my son had bought. We had run out of 'working capital', but it was not prudent to sell our lambs as we were under stocked and had an abundance of grass. They would be better fattened here on our own grass.

We had money to buy sheep at the sheep sales, but no other cash. The reason that we had money to buy sheep is that my son was about to spend his 'university fund'. From the day he was born until his 18th birthday the state provided 'family allowance'. Anticipating that the boys may want to go to university I had not spent a penny of this money, and put it into three separate saving accounts for them. When I began to save university education was free, now it is very costly, so despite Oscar having these savings

134

he will still leave university with a sizeable student debt. Hector had decided that he did not want to continue his education beyond eighteen, which gave him around £13,000 to spend on sheep. I was very glad that I had saved it.

We had a great crop of 'second cut' grass sitting in the meadows around our house, but no money to get a contactor to bale it. This grass should make money, as with it we could either overwinter other people's cows or sell it for money. Hector decided that he would cut all the grass himself, and borrowed a mower. He began the mammoth task of mowing on the 3 September as the weather looked set fair. He also found an old haybob to scale out the grass, so we only had to get the contactor to bale and wrap the silage bales. 'Scaling out' is when we turn the grass to help it dry before it is rowed up and baled. The machinery to do this is very expensive. How would we pay for the contactor? It would be about £500. We had no idea how we would pay it, but we had to carry on. We could not let the grass sit in the fields and waste the crop.

Hill farmers have always suffered from cash flow issues, as they get 'chunks' of money throughout the year and no reliable monthly income. The subsidy from the government for 2018, claimed in May, would be paid at the earliest in December. The money for the 2018 wool clip would be paid when the wool board received 2019's wool bag. Our biggest saleable assets, our lambs, are slow to mature in this upland environment and not worth as much as lowland lambs. It is a tricky business to manage the cash flow. We needed vaccines for the lambs, and food for some animals. We ordered it on account and kept on with our daily jobs, and tried not to worry about the finances. If worst came to worst we would have to sell the lambs 'store' for someone else to fatten, but that would mean that we got a lot less for them.

This does not seem to be the public's perception of hill farmers. They seem to think that we are awash with money from subsidies and that animal welfare is not a priority. As if sent specifically to illustrate this point, as soon as I typed the last sentence there was a knock at the door. It was a cyclist who enquired whether he was on the correct route to Sedbergh. When I told him that he was, he told me that he intended to report me as a sheep in a field was suffering, as despite me having loads of money I refused to pay £25 to call out a vet for it. He said that he had photographic evidence and the ear tag number.

It subsequently transpired that the sheep was on one of the other lots of our farm that had been sold to someone else. I tried to explain to him that the ear tag would identify where the animal was born but not necessarily to whom it belonged. He kept on saying that I was awash with cash and would not call the vet.

I tried to explain that you could not call your vet out to someone else's sheep, and that I was sure someone would come along and check it soon. Indeed, when I checked the field an hour later it was not there. I said to him that I was not swimming in cash, at which he laughed and said that all farmers say that, and if I actually was hard up and I could chop some of my trees down, and sell them for firewood for £70 a ton. I was about to say that the trees were valuable for wildlife, and anyway I did not have a log splitter or the qualifications to use a chainsaw, but he cycled off. His parting shot was "And I know where that £70 a ton will go, straight into your back pocket not declared as income."

It was rather an unpleasant situation to be criticized on your own doorstep, by a complete stranger, but I think it does serve to illustrate some members of the public's perception of hill farmers. I began to wonder if doctors and teachers and people of other professions are similarly harangued on their doorsteps. I hope not.

Meanwhile, while I was listening to a cyclist on the doorstep Hector was busy mowing. It took about fifteen hours to mow all of the grass, as there was an hour in the middle of the day to fix the mower. Fergus came in from school and began to scale out the grass that had been mowed early in the morning. They both finished working at 10pm, and left me the remainder of the fields to scale out the following day before the contractor came to bale them.

The new (old) tractor had different controls to the one I had driven at haymaking time, so Hector left me a postcard with a note about what each control did. If nothing else, I have had to drive a whole variety of vehicles that I have never driven before this year. If there is a job to be done there is no option but to get on and do it.

It took me five nerve-wracking hours to scale out all the grass, but I managed with my little postcard of instructions on the dashboard. No sooner had I finished and done the school run, than the contractors were here to bale and wrap the silage before the promised rain came. They finished at 10pm, another late night, and remarkably there were 129 big bales. This was a brilliant second crop, but also a very expensive second crop that would have to be paid for (about £1,300 pounds not £500), as well as the tank of diesel that we had ordered for the tractor to do the mowing and scaling out.

A small helping hand with the finances came in the form of the bacon that arrived from the butcher after having been cured. He said that it was the best bacon he had seen all year, and that I had sent the pig at exactly the right time, which apparently most people don't. I was really pleased with this feedback, and our customers seemed really pleased with the bacon as well.

Whilst you have a picture of me in your mind, driving around delivering packs of bacon, I think it is time to address another elephant in the room. Meat.

You may have read my first book *A Native Breed*, in which I state that at the age of four I made two silent promises to myself:

- When I had my own flock of sheep I would not be breeding mules, as if even the best boys are not good enough to keep that is something I did not want to be involved in.
- As soon as I was old enough to decide for myself, I would stop eating meat, especially lamb.

On the first promise, I can definitely say that my heart is still in breeding purebred sheep. I am very pleased with my Welsh Hill Speckle Faced tup lamb this year, and he will be used for breeding in the future. This is my main interest and passion, using native breeds to manage and maintain the environment that we know and love in Cumbria. The two go hand in hand, the native breeds have created the landscape and are needed to maintain it. I believe that it is also important to conserve the genetics of these hardy fell sheep that form the top tier of the stratified sheep system in the UK. The breeding and showing of these sheep are also crucial to our cultural heritage in Cumbria. Maintaining the farmer to manage the environment is also vital. The farmer has a skill set unique to his or her farm, and passes on those skills to his or her successor. It can be very difficult to take on an unknown farm, as I know.

That is not to say that there will be no cross-bred meat-producing sheep on our farm. There will be a balance. Hector's main interest is to produce top quality grass fed lamb. He is using native breeds put to terminal sires to do this. His interest is not in native plants and grasses, but in how the grassland can be rotationally grazed to benefit his livestock business model. In a nutshell, you could say that my sheep enterprises are decided mainly by my heart, and his by his head. I am hoping that the post Brexit farm subsidies will bring these two enterprises closer together and not drive them apart, I am hoping that we will be rewarded for biodiversity and using traditional breeds.

On the second promise, I did stop eating meat as soon as I was old enough to decide for myself. This was not only because of the incident that I described where my pet lamb was taken for meat, but also because where I lived as a child was next to a railway line that was used for transporting a lot of livestock. When my bedroom window was open at night on a hot evening I could hear the animals in the train making distressed noises. Sometimes the crossing would be closed and the train would have to stop, and you could see legs stuck out of the vents at odd angles. It seemed to me that livestock welfare was not a priority. I stopped eating meat on the basis that the food chain as I saw it was causing suffering to animals. I also had to pass a huge industrial pig farm on the way to school. I did not want to eat meat from animals that were produced industrially, and carted around squashed in trains at night.

I did not eat meat for 30 years, until we started to produce our own meat. I have responsibility for the birth, life and manner of death of each of my animals. On the last day of their lives that responsibility is passed to our local abattoir, but I personally deliver the animals to the abattoir and ensure that they are not stressed at all by the experience. Now, my life experience has taught me that we need to eat native breed animals or they will die out. Their reason for existence is that they are part of the food chain. If we want the landscapes that we love in Cumbria to continue, we need to eat the produce that creates that landscape.

A lot of animal rights groups now are not only advocating that we don't eat meat or other animal products, but that we do not keep animals on farms or even as pets. I love animals, and that is why I have resolved that I will have to eat my native breeds in order to ensure their survival. It is also important that I 'practice what I preach', if I am filling social media with images of delicious cuts of meats in order to try and get people to buy them from me, I need to commit to eating them myself.

I have accepted that it is very important to eat meat, for the sake of the survival of the animals themselves and for our landscape. As a family, we eat our own beef, pork and lamb. We are privileged to be in the position where we have absolute confidence in the food chain that we are part of, and I believe that the way ahead is for more people to make contact with a farmer that they know and trust, and buy meat directly from them. It doesn't matter if that is a local farmer, or one that they have interacted with online. We sell our meat at the same prices as local supermarkets, so it is affordable for most people.

On one of my farm walks, there was a young girl getting upset at the thought that one of the Dexter calves would eventually become meat. I tackled the issue head on, as we watched the calf running and jumping for joy along the riverbank. I told her that I was not upset at the thought of him becoming meat, because I have given him the best life that I can possibly could, and without the need for meat he would not exist. If we love our animals and want them to continue to graze our fells, turning grass into protein, we need to eat them.

It has taken me practically all of my life to come to this decision. Now I understand the food chain, and have control over it, I can see it is essential for our native breeds for people to eat them, and for the landscape that the animals maintain, which I love. When I met my husband I was eighteen, and used to say to him that I was going to write books. We have been married for 25 years, and over those years he would periodically ask me when the promised books were going to appear. I used to say that I didn't have enough life experience yet to write them, which he thought was a convenient excuse. It was not an excuse; I needed to experience life before I was confident enough to write about it. Similarly with the food chain, I now feel that after managing the land and keeping my own animals for over ten years that I am confident about eating our own meat. I needed the time to go on the journey, and understand it.

Maybe I am just a slow learner, but I like to think that I consider things carefully and act in the best interests of my animals and our landscape. Perhaps reading my books has helped you, the reader, to explore these ideas as well?

Back to 2018, the weather during the first week of September was glorious. Dewy mornings followed by sunny afternoons. I had two trips out, one with Antony to Moorcock Show, and one to a Challenge Sheep event. Moorcock Show is one of the oldest and most competitive sheep shows in the Yorkshire Dales. This year it was the 102nd show. It is held near Appersett, near the Moorcock Inn. As we approached the Moorcock Inn from Mallerstang a group of men came pouring out of the inn and down the steps towards the road. They were all wearing sheep breed society ties. When we got to the show people were patiently waiting for the judges to finish their lunch at the Moorcock Inn, so we were able to report that they were on their way.

There were lots of show classes for Swaledale Sheep, as you would expect in Swaledale. There were also Herd-wick, Rough Fell, Texel, Bluefaced Leicester and mule classes. Antony and I spent a happy hour watching the Herdwick judging and judging the sheep ourselves. We did not pick the same winners as the judge although we were both totally convinced of our choices.

There was music on the field from the Hawes town band, and it was a very enjoyable afternoon. Afterwards we went into Hawes to buy some Wensleydale cheese quiche for our lunch.

Challenge Sheep is not a competition; it is a project that aims to 'understand the consequences of the rearing phase in the lifetime performance of ewes.' It is tracking 9,000 sheep across the UK for several years in order to understand their performance. One of the farms in the project is in Windermere and there are regular events that farmers can participate in. All the events are free, funded by the Animal Health levy. This levy of 60p per head of sheep is paid by producers at the abattoir, and the money goes into the funding of education about sheep and cows. In my opinion it is excellent value for money. At the event as well as the activities that were set up for us we had access to a sheep specialist vet all day, to ask any questions that we had.

We were a motley collection of farmers with flocks from 20-1,200 sheep. It is good to have a day with other farmers, great to chat about different breeds of sheep. There were several differences of opinions about controversial topics such as whether sheep feet should be routinely trimmed, but such debate is very healthy in what can be a very insular profession.

The real challenge for me and my sheep this week, however, was the Westmorland Show. The Westmorland Show is a huge one day show attracting 30,000 visitors per year. It is quite expensive to enter sheep into the show (£14 for the first sheep and £4 for each subsequent sheep) and the show seems to have a more 'formal' competitive air about it than a local shepherds meet. People come from all over the country to show their sheep there.

Just as I was about to wash my sheep two days before the show I got a text message from Hector asking me to go to a postcode in Dumfriesshire and look at some sheep there that were for sale. He had seen them online, and it did make me wonder whether auction sales for breeding sheep would become a thing of the past, as this was the second time recently that we had seen sheep for sale online.

I thought that I could manage the journey there and back between my school run, and so had a whistle stop trip to Scotland. I picked out 27 Welsh Mountain sheep (some crossed with a Swaledale) and 15 Herdwicks, and arranged for them to be delivered at the weekend before dashing back to Cumbria.

The agreement was that if I went to look at the sheep, Hector would not be cross with me if the sheep were not properly prepared for the show. I washed them the following day, and practiced holding them. One of the sheep was still quite flighty, but they looked reasonably clean.

We loaded them at 7am, and set off for the show. Sheep showing commenced at 9.30, and at 9.15 we pulled onto the showground. It had taken us more than two hours to travel fourteen miles to the show because of the show traffic. Particularly terrifying had been the queue actually on the motorway in the inside lane. I was worried that a lorry would crash into the standing traffic.

As we only had fifteen minutes to spare I leapt out of the Land Rover and ran off with the sheep, a bucket and cloths, and two flasks of hot water to clean them in their pens. I was so absorbed in what I was doing that I didn't notice that Hector was unable to start the Land Rover to drive away from the unloading area and was causing a tailback of sheep owners unable to unload. A wire had come off from the starter motor and the Land Rover could not start.

He had to get people to push start him, which is no easy task for a Land Rover with a huge sheep trailer on (the small one still being a home with a collapsed wheel bearing). Every time I attempt to show sheep there seems to be some drama.

Thankfully a mechanic friend of Hector's was based on a stand at the show. He knew immediately what the problem would be and they were able to fix it before we needed to load the sheep again.

Showing the sheep did not go badly; in big classes of eight to fourteen we got fourth and fifth. Rosettes are awarded for up to fifth place at the county show so I was pleased to be 'in the ribbons'. Hector was not happy as the sheep did not stand still, but we had had given it a go. Most of the other sheep in our 'Any Other Breed' class were various breeds of Texel sheep, and the judge said to me that while I had very good sheep he had to judge them on what would sell best commercially. I thought that the idea was to judge the sheep from the breed society's breed standard, but whatever the criteria mountain sheep are always going to be more flighty than lowland sheep as over the years they will have been much less handled as a breed.

Mountain sheep, like mountain shepherds, have to be strong, independent and willing to set their own agenda. This self-reliant nature is crucial for the survival of both the human and the ovine species. Both sheep and shepherd need the ability to think on their feet and react to the weather and circumstances around them. This September it felt as if there was a new challenge arising every day. It felt as if we were responding to challenges, and not anticipating them, but there was no option other than to keep on with our regular daily jobs and respond to other challenges as they arose.

Farm Walks

The day after the Westmorland Show I was exhausted, but there were jobs to do and I had to get on with them. I loaded up the quad with animal food and set off down to Low Park to feed the cows. We still had a courtesy quad, as ours was being repaired (again). The fuel gauge on the courtesy quad did not work, and it had a few quirks, such as having to be on reserve fuel mode all the time or it would not start. Normally with a quad you have to physically turn the handle onto reserve fuel and this alerts you to the fact that there is little fuel left if you have ignored the fuel gauge.

I'm sure you can guess what happened, I was stranded three and a half miles from home with only an hour to get back home before going on my school run after running out of petrol. It may have been only three and a half miles to run, but I was in huge boots and waterproofs, and there are three very steep hills to go up.

I decided to try and avoid these hills by travelling along the riverbank. I hadn't been that way through the woods for at least a month, and was horrified to find a large area of Himalayan balsam growing in a gully. Himalayan balsam is a non-native, invasive plant. It was introduced by Victorian seed collectors, but is so large that it can erode riverbanks and cause flooding by blocking waterways. That must be why I ran out of petrol, so that I could find the Himalayan balsam. It was too late to do anything about it this year, but next year we will have to remove it. The Lune Rivers Trust has a team of volunteers who can come and help us with this in the spring. They have removed other areas of these plants along the Lune, and are keen to make sure that it does not out compete all our native plants.

I photographed the Himalayan balsam, and then sped on. I arrived home in 58 minutes, and was only ten minutes late to school. The quad had to be left out overnight, and I had a bizarre dream about cows eating it, but thankfully all was well.

The following day, Saturday, we got all of our breeding sheep into the old sheep pen down at Low Park. Hector was not happy with the body condition score of some of the sheep, they were too thin. We had wormed them, and they did not have messy bums, so we decided to give them all a dose of fluke medicine and a bolus. The fluke is a horrible little parasite that the sheep can ingest from puddles and wet areas, as it inhabits snails for part of its life cycle. It then damages the sheep's liver.

We had already bolused the lambs, but not the mature sheep. We like to do this at the end of summer to bring the sheep into top condition before they meet the tup. Our sheep pens at Low Park were not ideal for handling sheep easily, so Hector quickly set up a temporary footbath and race using hurdles tied together.

All the sheep went through the footbath, and any lame sheep were pulled out and treated. Two were found to have maggots in their feet and needed immediate attention. You can never be complacent with sheep; there are always checks to be made and jobs to do. The key is to observe the sheep very closely, as they perceive you as a predator and are very reluctant to show any sign of illness or injury if they can avoid it.

After working our way through the sheep we had to dash back home because Hector was going to the after show party at the Westmorland Show, and we were holding a barbeque for the members of Borrowdale Fell Running Club. Antony was pleased because one of the members has a business where he tests outdoor clothing, and brought a pile of down jackets for the runners to test for him. The (sustainably sourced) down had been waterproofed, and he wanted to know if it would go into 'clumps' after a while. After the barbeque I had to drive to the party (in my pyjamas) to collect Hector in the early hours of the morning.

The following day, Sunday, was another Open Farm day. It dawned very wet, but by the time the first visitors arrived at 10.30am it was drying up. I had to have competed my farm work and dog walking by 10.30, as the rest of the day would be occupied talking to visitors. The Lunesdale Archaeological Trust and a photographer friend came to set up stands, and I was selling mutton, pork, knitted goods, etc.

The first walk went well, and there was just time for a quick sandwich before we set off on the afternoon walk. On the walk I try to explain to the visitors how I plan to balance the historic, agricultural and environmental needs of the land. It is no easy task. We set off and walk around the Roman fort first, and talk about the history of the farm from when the Romans arrived in 70AD to the present day.

I then take the visitors alongside the River Lune and explain about how we plan to manage existing and create more riparian strips along the riverbank. I was just about

to talk about the wildlife that we have on the farm currently, when right on cue three otters swam over and climbed out onto the riverbank about five meters from where we were standing.

The river was gushing along and there were a series of rapids around the meander at the bottom of the Roman fort area. In a fascinating glimpse into their world, we all stood and watched the adult otters teaching the pup to swim in fast water. The adults would slide in, and tread water several feet from the riverbank calling to their pup. The pup would stand on the riverbank peeping and wailing, not wanting to jump in. They would keep encouraging him to come in, and eventually he would. They would then all swim together in the rapids for a couple of minutes, before sliding out on the riverbank. Once on the riverbank again the pup would tell them a real tale, and they would listen sympathetically before jumping back into the river and calling him in again. It was a privileged view of an otter's swimming lesson, maybe a once in a lifetime chance to see an otter family interacting together for most of the visiting group. I didn't need to say much about the wildlife on the farm, we were all awestruck by what we had seen.

Also right on time, as I began to talk about the three tier sheep system, and how we were buying draft sheep from the fells, a trailer load of newly bought sheep from Scotland arrived. After the visitors had seen them, and bought pork and mutton to take home, the new sheep were walked down to Low Park farm before nightfall. One way and another it had been quite an epic day.

I was hoping for an early night, but one of the videos that the visitors had posted online of the otters swimming was generating a lot of interest. Paul Ross, Talk Radio presenter and brother of Jonathan Ross, emailed to ask if I could talk about wildlife on our farm at 11pm.

He explained that he was going to be talking to Chris Packham, the BBC presenter who had recently launched a Manifesto for Wildlife and was planning a walk for wildlife in London. Paul wanted someone to talk about how farmers value wildlife, and in return he would mention my books and farm walks. So when everyone else was fast asleep I was sitting next to the Rayburn in the kitchen waiting for the phone to ring.

I spoke positively about the wildlife on our farm for about fifteen minutes with Paul. I think it is important to put the farmer's view across. In the manifesto for wildlife

Mark Avery who was writing about the ecology of the uplands stated that the Government should: 'Maintain voluntary grant schemes for environmental action on upland farms but only on the basis that each payment is a down payment on eventual purchase by the taxpayer.'

So, under that scenario if I ask Natural England for help to provide stability along the riverbank by planting trees and providing cover for the otters, and assisting in flood alleviation, they can only help me if I agree to our farm being compulsorily purchased. How could a farmer with a mortgage possibly agree to that? Surely if we want to provide habitats for wildlife we need to offer schemes and funding solutions that are attractive to farmers for maximum uptake. This idea would certainly not be attractive to any upland farmer that I know.

He also suggested that some areas of overgrazing by sheep should be maintained as a lesson to the future in how not to manage land. The manifesto is not only misguided in my opinion, but is also completely disregarding the cultural heritage of upland farming. The families involved in upland farming have again been forgotten. Somebody needs to make the case for us, which is why I am sitting by my fire in the middle of the night discussing otter habitats on national radio. It's a funny old world.

Something that I did not find funny was when the Wildlife Trust posted a photo on their Twitter feed reporting on the manifesto and subsequent walk for wildlife in London of a man carrying a placard saying 'owls not cows'. Again images like this will alienate farmers, and surely conservation organisations and farmers need to work together for a sustainable future for wildlife? After a 'discussion' on Twitter with the Wildlife Trust they removed the image, and stated that they do not agree with the policy of compulsorily purchasing upland farms if they access environmental funding. Exchanges like this are unnecessary and exhausting. I am trying to balance the historical, environmental and commercial aspects of my farm as well as I can, as are thousands of other farmers. We need to work together with conservation organisations not be demonised by them.

After the late night we were up bright and early the next morning as Hector wanted to make some sheep pens for the new sheep down at Low Park Farm. Sheep pens are an area where you can gather your sheep into, and handle them safely. It much better for the sheep to be unable to run about when you are trying to give them medication, so a 'race' is usually at one side of the pens. This is a long corridor that the sheep can walk in and out of, while you treat them en route. There needs to be a gate at either end so that the shepherd can let sheep in and out.

There is usually a frame above the race so that you can hang medications up. Medication such as sheep wormer comes in a big (usually 2.2 litre) plastic container. You attach a hose and a 'gun' to the end. The gun is calibrated and you set it to the right amount. To do this you usually need to know roughly how much the sheep weighs, so that for example if it is 70kg you need to give the sheep 7ml of wormer. If it weighs 60kg you need to give it 6ml of wormer, etc.

It sounds like a complicated set up, but it was relatively easy to construct once we had planned it out. We re-used as many materials as we could from around the farm, and made the little gates from plywood. The whole set up cost us £36 to construct. We even used some bags of gravel for the floor of the race that the council had left on our land before we bought it and forgotten about.

The pens and the race were all ready for use, so the following day we were again up bright and early to test them out. We wanted them to be able to be used by two people, myself and Hector. At our previous farm the land and pens were such that we always needed three people to gather into the pens, and this meant that we could only really do it during weekends and school holidays.

Thankfully all went according to plan, and of the 125 breeding ewes that we had on the farm at this time, we gathered in 124 into the pens. Once the sheep were in, uncounted, Hector said, "How confident are you that we have all the sheep here?" and I said "99 per cent, there's one I can't see." Remarkably I was right, we later spotted her sitting by the River Lune; oblivious to what she had missed.

The sheep fitted nicely into one of the three pens, which was ideal as hopefully this time the following week we would have about three times as many sheep. We bolused and fluked all the new sheep from Scotland in the new race, and ran them through the footbath. During the afternoon a very ferocious storm blew up, and we were glad to get back home, and settled into the lounge with the curtains drawn as night fell.

Suddenly Ruby started barking at something outside, and then there was a knock at the door. Antony said, "Well this isn't going to be someone with good news" and we opened the door to a farmer from a few miles away saying, "Do you keep Herefords?" Some young cattle had somehow escaped from another farm and were running about in the road outside our house, so it was waterproofs back on, and out to walk them back towards the Howgills and away from the danger of being on the road. Meanwhile the farmer who had found them got on the phone, and found out whose they were. When I had walked them about twenty minutes down the road I could hear a quad bike coming through the darkness somewhere. Another farmer with his dog appeared, and moved them along.

"Will you manage now?" I shouted into the darkness

"Yes, lass, I'll manage" and off they went. Nobody ignores the knock on the door or the phone call to say stock is out, because next time it will probably be your cows. We are a community, and we work together whether we like it or not. It's just the way it is, and the way it has to be.

Breeding Sheep

Before we could turn our attention to the purchase of more breeding sheep at the big Swaledale and Rough Fell sheep sale on the last Friday in September, we had first to buy some tups. We needed a variety of tups for different purposes, each ewe had to be matched to an appropriate tup to breed a useful lamb. I had long since realised that it was pointless to breed lambs that nobody wanted to buy.

We would be putting 300 ewes to tups this year, and of these 300, fourteen would be Ouessants. I had one older Ouessant tup, Millican Dalton, who I would use for as long as possible on any unrelated females, and needed another tup to join him to breed from his daughters who were now in the flock. There was no point in looking in local auctions, so I advertised online for a tup, and a farm park in Durham had six that they were looking to sell. After a long exchange of photos the tup that I chose was 'unproven', meaning that he had never bred before, so I also chose another older, proven tup to come along with him. The farm park delivered both tups for £200 which I thought was very good value. Thankfully I had sold quite a few hats and a scarf online that week and had made enough to cover the cost of the tups.

The tups arrived and seemed ideal, and we introduced them to Millican Dalton. Millican Dalton may be the smallest tup on the farm, but he is also the tup with the most attitude. If it looks like tups are going to fight (to work out who is the boss) then it is advisable to put them into a small enclosed area while they work it out. I was reluctant to do this as I had once put a tup lamb that I had sold online into a pen with Millican Dalton while his new owner came to collect the tup lamb. I went back outside twenty minutes later and Millican Dalton was stood, looking as if butter wouldn't melt, over the dead body of the tup lamb.

It looked as if the tups were going to settle, accepting Millican Dalton as the boss, so I left them in the pony field with the other tups for the evening. In the morning the other tups were stood at the gate, waiting for me to come along, but there was no sign of Millican Dalton or the new tups. It became apparent that they were engaged in a dramatic warfare game, by which they would stalk, chase and head butt each other to prove who was the biggest/fastest/strongest Ouessant tup. They played this game for two days, during which they all sustained cuts to their faces, then they settled down quietly again and were waiting at the gate the next morning for me. It was a good job that they had another month to rest before they met the female Ouessants, it must have exhausted them.

My Welsh sheep would be going to a pure Welsh tup that I had bought the previous year, and I also had my Welsh tup lamb that I was very fond of. The purpose of the Welsh lambs was to build a flock for the future; the gimmer lambs would become the breeding ewes in the flock. I didn't have enough Welsh lambs this year for my plans, so I had arranged for fifteen to be bought from Snowdonia and delivered on the day of the Rough Fell ewe sale. I had also arranged to buy 25 older Welsh ewes. I liked the Welsh sheep as, like the Herdwicks, they kept their weight on in the winter and seemed to be able to survive on minimal grazing. Unlike the Herdwicks they did not seem to escape at every opportunity.

I also had ten Ryeland/Shetland ewes and they would be going to my Ryeland tup that I had bought the previous year. The purpose of these lambs would be to increase my fibre flock, to produce knitting wool. This year those ten sheep had had eleven lambs, but only three of them were Ryeland girls, so more were required. There is a minimum quantity of wool (20kg) that the mill will accept, so I needed more fleeces for this project.

The remainder of the sheep were pure bred mountain ewes: Herdwicks, Rough Fells, Swaledales and Welsh Mountains. Of these, some would be going to a Rough Fell tup given to us by the breed secretary, and the rest would go to 'terminal sires'. The very best Rough Fell Sheep and a few Swaledales as an experiment would go to the Rough Fell tup. These would provide the flock replacements for the breeding ewes of the future, along with my Welsh Speckles. The boy lambs from these would take longer to mature than the commercial lambs, and these would be fed only on grass/hay with mineral supplements as appropriate. They would probably then be sold as grass fed meat boxes to internet customers.

That left the mountain ewes crossed to the terminal sires. A terminal sire is a meaty tup, producing a sturdy lamb to be sold for meat. Both the male and female commercial lambs are sold as meat. They will hopefully be mature enough to sell at around 40kg around November 2019.

We needed to buy some terminal sire tups. Last year the

Herdwicks that we bought had been to a Beltex/Charolais tup, and my son felt that the Herdwicks struggled to lamb two weighty lambs to this tup. He wanted to buy Texel tups with small heads, and went to Bentham auction to a big tup sale with friends and a shared trailer. He bought four large tups with relatively small heads and was very pleased with them. Thankfully he was paid the night before the sale so that he could afford to buy the tups, which averaged at £300 each.

In contrast to my fighting Ouessant tups, these boys were very chilled from the off. No fighting, they were quite happy to live in the farmyard and 'lean to' eating hay and food. They were resting up for the big job that was ahead of them. Hector would also need to buy another couple of tups to follow on and 'jack up' any sheep that did not get pregnant in the first cycle of tupping for one reason or another, but for now everything was coming together.

We also had a visit from a farmer who wanted 25 cows overwintering at £10.50 per cow per week, so we could see that we would be able to pay the bill for the silage once the cows came indoors in November. The *Daily Mail* and other newspapers were running their annual story that it was going to be the coldest winter ever, and so just to terrify ourselves before we went to bed one night we watched a documentary on the winter of 1947. I drifted off to sleep thinking thank goodness we have big barns and everything can come inside if it needs to.

I didn't sleep the night before the Rough Fell ewe sale. I was so concerned about what the price would be, and whether we would be able to buy the sheep that we needed. We were up early, getting all the farming jobs done so that we could take delivery of the Welsh sheep before 10.30am and then leave for the sale, judging of the sheep started at 11am.

The Welsh sheep arrived right on time, and the 25 ewes and fifteen gimmer lambs raced out of the trailer and into the Bridge Field next to the house where they would wait until we got back from the sale. They all looked well, and we had agreed a price in advance. This purchase cleaned out my building society savings account; I actually had one pound left. I had no money to spend at the sale; it would be Hector who would be buying sheep with his savings from the family allowance child benefit.

Judging was underway when we got to the sale, and the first of the 6,000 Swaledale sheep were already being sold. My first thought when looking at the Rough Fell pens was that there were not many sheep here. The Rough Fell is a minority breed, and there were 820 breeding sheep in the sales catalogue, but there were nowhere near that amount actually at the sale. A friend explained that people often enter a lot more than they are going to bring so that they are allocated more pens in the auction and their sheep can be seen easily. We wanted to buy 100 shearlings, sheep about eighteen months old, so that we could breed flock replacements from them for at least four years. It looked as if there were only about 100 shearlings in the sale. We would have to buy everything that we liked that came into the ring, whatever the price.

Hector looked through all of the sheep on sale, and discounted some, as he did not like their teeth. Teeth are very important in sheep grazing on poorer grasses in the uplands. Hector does not like sheep with long teeth, as he believes that they will snap off easily. A sheep without teeth to eat grass efficiently will die on our farm.

The Rough Fell sheep were being sold after the Swaledales. It was a long, four and a half hour wait until the first Roughs came into the ring. The loudspeaker announced that the sale of Rough Fell Sheep was about to start, and remaining Swaledale farmers left their seats, and Hector went and stood right at the edge of the ring. All I could do was sit and watch, it was his money, his decision and ultimately it would be his future flock that he was building.

The first group of sheep to come into the ring were from the same breeder who had bred my first ten Rough Fell sheep, including my favourite sheep Squiggle. I had paid £92 each for them four years ago, how would they sell today? Thankfully they were not as expensive, and Hector bought them for £65 each, "sold Hector Meanwell". That was what we needed to hear. The next group to come into the ring were also the correct age, £70, "sold Hector Meanwell". There was then a neighbour of ours with 30 sheep of the right age, £70, "sold Hector Meanwell."

Not everything went his way, several pens were out of his price range at £105 and £130 per sheep, but at the end of the sale he had bought 62 sheep at an average price of £66 each. That was a success, and he did two trips home with the trailer to bring them home while I went on my school run. The sheep were then let out into the temporary field with the Welsh sheep until the morning.

A good omen came in his 'luck money'. This is money given to the buyer by the seller of sheep in the hope that the sheep will do well for them. In with his luck money

Hector got a 50p with Peter Rabbit on. He has a collection of 50p pieces, and he was missing this one! It had to be a good sign.

We were up bright and early the next day to sort out the sheep. The gimmer lambs had to be separated from the adult sheep and given a bolus, and marked with our flock mark. They were then put in with our other lambs. Currently all the commercial lambs and flock replacements were together, but the time was approaching when we would need to separate them and begin selling commercial lambs.

Not today though, because we had plenty to do. The sheep were all gathered into some make shift pens that we constructed near the farm from sheep hurdles. Mum and Dad came to help, and operated the gates at the front and back of the race. About six sheep were put into the race at one time, and then were given wormer, flukicide, a bolus and our flock mark. They were then let out onto the track to Low Park Farm.

Once all 62 Roughs and 25 Welsh had been through the pens, we walked them in a big group for about a mile down the River Lune. Ultimately they needed to go right down to Low Park, but they could rest here for a couple of days after being brought to a new farm. A three and a half mile walk may have been too much for them on top of everything else.

We then had a look through the auction catalogue for the Rough Fell Sheep sale, and noticed that a farm a couple of miles away had entered sheep but had not been at the sale. Hector rang them and arranged to go around that evening; he picked out fifteen ewes that he liked.

Sunday morning saw us again up bright and early head-ing round the Howgill Fells with our sheep trailer. The ewes were slightly older than we would have liked, but of excellent quality. He had to pay a little more for them, but really liked them. Again they were put into our temporary sheep pens and given our marker before being let out onto our farm. We had run out of boluses, so would have to do them later in the week.

It was the last day of September, a day of sunshine and showers, double rainbows arched over the Howgill Fells. September, you had exhausted me, but we were well on the way to stocking our farm. We probably needed to find about another 50 sheep to put to the tup this year. Before the long winter would be here, and we would begin our winter-feeding routine.

The house, heated by only one Rayburn stove in the kitchen, was feeling cold in the evenings. Once everyone else had gone to bed I sat in my writing room with a coat and hat on over my clothes typing this book. I tried to record every decision that we had to make; historical, en-vironmental or agricultural, so that you could read about it. The key was to learn from mistakes, because there was no doubt that in our first year here many mistakes would be made.

The archaeological dig had started at my neighbour's farm, and the Lunesdale Archaeological Trust were not using our farm to host open days as planned. As they had not offered any explanation of this decision I felt confused, and a little cheated when visitors to the archaeological dig showed me emails telling them to park outside our house. Initially we had agreed that everyone could use our yard/field for parking, and one of our buildings for finds washing and open days. I looked on the archaeological society website and noticed with dismay that there were to be no open days at the dig because of limited parking.

I then felt disappointed that the public would not be able to access the dig, confused that it had been taken away from us without explanation, and cheated that I had written to the Heritage Lottery fund on their behalf asking for funding for the dig as I would provide parking/open days/social media updates. I guess coming into a new area and dealing with people with whom I had no previous relationship would always throw up challenges. This was particularly disappointing because of my background in archaeology, which at last had appeared to be for some purpose-to engage the public with our Roman Fort.

There were bound to be failures as well as successes this first year. Perhaps I needed to look to another archaeological society to build a relationship with. I was hopeful that the fort could be used to engage the public in both history and the environment in the Yorkshire Dales National Park; I just had to work out how.

October

*Nearly always, the fells and the weather
do their best to be friends in October
Below Scafell (1955) Dudley Hoys*

October dawned cold and fresh. As I stood in the farmyard
with Ruby at 7.17am waving to Antony's train to Glasgow
as it passed, everywhere was frozen. Winter was coming,
there was no mistaking it. A solitary roe deer stag stood on
the horizon, master of all he surveyed. I imagined him anticipating the arrival of winter; he must be able to feel that
it is coming too. Autumn is a very short season in the uplands; it passes through the valley like an express train.

The first day of October was again busy for us. The new
sheep that we had bought after the Rough Fell sale had to
be gathered in and bolused, and all the lambs moved to
fresh grazing. Everything went according to plan, and that
left half a day for 'wooding'. Hector had been trimming
overhanging branches from the woodland strips at the edge
of the meadows at Low Park Farm.

After we had eaten our lunch of bacon and egg sandwiches (that had been wrapped in tin foil) by the riverbank
Hector announced that he was going to try and drive
through the old ford. The previous owners had used a ford
across the river Lune for years for getting to and from Low
Park Farm, rather than the long, bumpy track. We hadn't

yet tried driving through the river.

Hector went first in the tractor and made it safely. He then tried on the quad and turned back, it was too small a vehicle for the large stones on the riverbank. We loaded our trailer with wood, and Hector set off on his first journey loaded up across the river. Thankfully it went smoothly and he got home much quicker in the tractor that way. That was the way to access the lower meadows in the future. From there we could quickly get up on to the Fairmile Road and home.

As we travelled home it was getting very chilly. I had a woollen scarf pulled up over my face, and a hat pulled low to just above my eyes. As we stopped to open the yard gate Hector said, "I'm really hoping my premium bonds come up Mum, then the first thing I'm going to buy is a gator so you don't get cold."

A gator is a small agricultural vehicle that is as agile as a quad but has a small cab on the top to keep off the wind. I wasn't actually feeling cold, but comments like that make you feel warm inside.

Something that did not make me feel warm inside was when we found out the following morning that the archaeologists' equipment had been stolen from the field where they were working overnight. The initial plan had been for them to leave their equipment locked up in one of our farm buildings, but as this arrangement had fallen through for reasons unknown they had apparently left their equipment in a mini marquee and trailer on the field. The trailer had been stolen.

It was not a nice thought to think that somebody had been around in the valley during the night looking for things to steal. The archaeological dig seemed to be going ahead anyway, as cars were still parking on the grass outside our house and walking down to the dig. It felt a bit petty of me to inwardly moan to myself about cars churning up my newly mown grass when they had had their equipment stolen.

We also had a contractor repairing the bridge at the bottom of the farm, and they were parking at the bottom of one of our fields and siting their welfare cabin there. Two more teams of workmen for Network Rail, with their own welfare cabins, were coming later on in the month. I had never expected that there would be such a lot of negotiating to do over access/parking at this farm. In Rusland the only negotiations I can remember about access were about hound trialling (racing over fells with dogs following an aniseed trail). I had never taken an interest in hound trialling, but it is a Cumbrian tradition stretching back over the centuries. The hound trialling community were very grateful to me for allowing access, and insisted that I come and judge their puppy show.

The contractors repairing the bridge had to remove seven trees, which they cut into manageable sized logs for us to use as firewood. I wouldn't have chosen to remove the trees, so at least we benefitted in some way. The roots were apparently making the riverbank unstable, which in turn could affect the bridge, so as part of a flood alleviation strategy they had to be removed.

There were some very wet days in October, with the rain blowing in great swathes down the valley. Low cloud meant low visibility; it was difficult to check the animals quickly in the wind and the rain. I was on the farm on my own for most days, Hector being busy with employment on other farms. As we do not have a television, and the internet connection is not good enough to read a newspaper online easily, let alone download a video to watch, it could have been easy to feel quite cut off from the world around me.

Most days I only talked to my own family. As Fergus was in his last year at school he had not changed schools when we moved due to the disruption that this would cause to his GCSE study, so I had around three hours in the car each day going to and from Windermere. There is no radio signal in our valley because of the shape of the gorge, so once I was out of the top of the valley and on my way to deliver or collect him, I looked forward to listening to Radio 4 and finding out what was going on in the world.

There was still a lot of cleaning up and sorting out to do on the farm. One Sunday I decided to try and clean out the old shippons. These are areas under the hayloft where years ago would have been housed for the winter, tethered around the neck. It is very dark in the shippons; it takes a while for your eyes to adjust to the light.

They are located underneath the old hay barn, so that the heat from the cows' bodies would have helped to keep the hay dry, the cows warm and it was easier to feed them by dropping hay through a special trap door. As you walk in there is a central passage, concreted with a drain in so that it can easily be cleaned out. On either side there are wooden stalls with cobbled floors where the cows would have been housed.

There is also a third row of stalls on one side. The cobbles were encrusted in dried on cow muck, and I wanted to clean them so that we could we could use the area for storage. Several hours with a hosepipe, brush and shovel and I had cleaned one of the rows. Fergus had cooked us a Sunday roast with one of our pork joints, and we had just sat down to eat it when the phone rang. It was one of our neighbours saying that he had not seen his dogs since yesterday, and he was heading down to Low Park Farm as someone had seen some of our sheep in the river.

Another neighbour phoned to say that there were definitely sheep in the river, possibly standing on rocks and unable to move. It had been raining steadily all afternoon, and the river would be gushing by now. We set off in the Land Rover and on the quad, just as it was getting dark. We met the neighbour with the missing dogs, who said he couldn't see anything amiss. We decided to walk further down the river, and then saw one of our sheep dead in the water. She had large bites on her rear end, with her internal organs pulled out. The two dogs were sitting next to the sheep under a fallen tree.

I was very upset as this was one of my original sheep, one of the first ten Rough Fell Sheep that I had bought at auction in 2014. For four years that sheep had been a faithful member of the flock, part of my team, and had never put a foot wrong. She had reared lambs every year. She did not deserve to be eaten by a dog. Of course it was impossible for us to prove whether the sheep had been chased into the river by the dogs or not. It was possible that she had ventured into the river by herself, and they had found her dead and eaten her. Possible, but not very likely. Contrary to popular opinion, sheep are not stupid.

We put the dogs in the back of our Land Rover, and

were about to try and jump start my neighbour's quad that had refused to start at this point, when we heard loud shouting from the riverbank. Somebody was on the other side of the river shouting "Come down, come down". It was the other neighbour who had rung because he had seen the sheep in the river.

We went right to edge of the river, and there was another barely alive sheep, bitten. I said, "Well she has clearly been bitten" and my neighbour said, "Definitely a wound of some sort." My priorities at this time were all about the sheep. We had to get this sheep back home as soon as possible and get her in a secure, warm place with something to eat. She was shaking badly, and obviously in shock. I kept talking to her and stroking her head. The battle to stay alive was as much psychological as physical. I knew from experience how easily sheep could give up on life.

You may wonder that I did not shout at my neighbour, or threaten to shoot his dogs, but to be honest a great sadness engulfed me, not a rage. After we had settled the sheep into the hay barn with water, hay and sheep food, I went back into the shippons and spent an hour on my hands and knees getting tiny bits of cow muck out from between cobbles. I hung a torch from the roof and worked away in silence and partial darkness. Only when my hands were raw and I felt exhaustion taking over, did I go back into the house and into bed. This was not a time for shouting, or taking to Twitter to berate people. It could easily have been one of my animals misbehaving, and we had to live alongside our neighbour. I shut the shippon door and said, to nobody in particular, "why do I bother?"

I couldn't sleep that night. I had the image of finding

the sheep and the dogs on the riverbank in my head constantly. I got up early and went to see how the sheep was doing. She was alive but couldn't stand. I gave her some sheep nuts, secure in the knowledge that she was a greedy old girl and would eat them when I was out of sight.

After breakfast I came back with my little dog Ruby. It may have seemed like a very mean strategy, but I knew that this sheep would stand if she could at the sight of a dog, as she would not be terrified of dogs. I told Ruby to stand at the door, and watched as the sheep tried to stand. She tried, but could not straighten her legs for some reason.

"Good girl" I said, stroking her head. I knew now that she had some fighting spirit. She had wanted to get up and away from Ruby, so that was half the battle. After lunch I went back again and held her while she tried to stand, not yet, but she was definitely trying.

At teatime I walked into the cowshed and she was standing, very wobbly, but she was standing. She sank to the floor after about half a minute, and I took her hay, sheep nuts and water.

"Tomorrow" I told her, "you're going outside." I left the cowshed doors open so that she could go out into the yard and eat grass if she wanted to overnight.

The next morning she was standing again, so I coaxed her to the door of the shed with sheep nuts. She stood on the threshold on very wobbly legs, she looked left and she looked right, then she put her head down and stood still. She was looking for her sister, who had died in the attack. They had never been apart before.

"Come on Lady, I'm still here" I said, and sat on the grass. Remarkably, on wobbly legs, she walked across the yard and started eating the grass next to me. If this was a psychological battle to live, it had been won. I just had to hope and pray that her injuries did not get infected and would heal properly. For the rest of the day I stayed in and around the farmyard, and she wandered in and out of the building to see me, eat grass, and then go back inside and rest.

Some people will say that farmers don't really care about their animals and have no relationship with them, they are just commodities to make money from. All I can do is tell you about things as they happen to me, and how I feel. I felt absolutely horrified and in shock after the dog attack, and absolutely exhausted with worry about the sheep for the following few days. I was so upset that the other sheep had been killed. You could say that ultimately I was going to take that sheep to the abattoir and she would have been killed for meat at the end of her breeding life. That is of course true, but I would have taken her to the abattoir in a trailer that was familiar to her and she would have had very little anxiety about what was going to happen, as she would be unaware of what was going on.

Instead she died with two dogs chasing her into a river, which must have been an extremely stressful situation, and she was then eaten, possibly while she was still alive. I felt terrible that this had happened to her and she had died in a very unpleasant way. She had trusted us to keep her safe on the farm, and one way or another humans had let her down.

After two days I decided to let the other sheep re-join the flock. She was still very stiff on her legs, but was constantly looking around for the company of other sheep, and

I thought that being back in the flock would be a tonic for her. It took her three hours from the farmhouse to slowly make her way back down to the riverbank, but then headed off following the other sheep. I hoped that she would make a complete recovery.

Meanwhile I continued to clean the muck off the shippon floors, and a beautiful cobbled floor emerged slowly but surely. There was also a big team effort by the Meanwell men (Hector, both grandads and uncle) to re concrete the barn floors in the cow barn ready for the cows to come in, which was anticipated on 1st November.

Everything was now gearing up for getting ready for winter. The buildings were almost ready for the cows to come in, and the grass had just about stopped growing. On 10 October we had to take the first bale of silage out to the cows. How long they would stay out would be dependant on ground conditions. The ground was not too wet at the moment.

The lambs did not appear to be growing now that the grass had stopped growing, and so early one morning Hector and I gathered them in and brought them into the yard for worming. We put them into the little lean to building, and sorted into one section the gimmer lambs that we wanted to keep as flock replacements. We had already marked these with a purple dot the last time we had the sheep in. There were 31 excluding the Ouessants. I had also arranged to buy another two privately, so if all went according to plan that should mean that we did not need to buy any additional sheep next year. We sent the girls back out, and then Hector sorted out his Beltex/Charolais/Herdwick lambs. They were almost fat enough to go to auction now, so he decided to keep them inside to fatten. These were not the lambs that we would hopefully sell next year as pasture fed hogget, so it was fine for them to stay inside and eat our lovely meadow hay and sheep cake.

Later that afternoon our lorry load of straw arrived, for animal bedding for the winter. It had been grown near Hull in North Yorkshire. By evening the lambs were all happy and cosy in the straw, chewing their cud after eating hay. Winter was now imminent. We were prepared, we had straw, hay, silage and buildings that were ready to accommodate stock if needed. As part of our sustainably/self sufficiency in the future we could do with a way to produce the animal bedding ourselves, as this was the only thing that had to be bought in from elsewhere, apart from the sheep cake for fattening Hector's lambs.

In our barn we had a bracken sledge. Originally the animal bedding used on this farm would have been bracken cut from the fell sides and brought back to the farm by pony sledge. Hector spent an hour talking to a neighbour about how he had harvested bracken from the fells about 50 years ago. It seemed possible, sustainable and a good use of a local resource. It seemed as if in future years we would go 'back to the future', and help make our farm future proof by using traditional farming methods coupled with modern machinery to make the job of baling the bracken easier. The key to our success or failure would be working with nature, not fighting against it.

Storms

The power of nature was about to be illustrated in a spectacular storm (Storm Callum) on 13 October. It had been raining constantly with very high winds all night, and when we got up on Saturday morning the 'lean to' building housing the straw was flooded, and some of the hay that had been stored in the silage pit had collapsed and was wet. We moved the straw, but the more pressing issue was that the back garden, an area enclosed on three sides by walls, was flooded.

The floodwater from the back garden had also flooded the small room called the 'cellar', although it is actually above ground. This room was used for storing food and beer for the coaching inn. The rainwater was still pouring into the garden, and it was lapping at the back doorstep.

Antony went off to buy a pump, to pump out the garden and prevent it from getting into the house, while my parents and I tried to unblock drains, and work out where the drains went. We were not making much progress with this, so I decided to go for a drive to check how the land was looking. I got as far as Carlingill, where a big stream gushes down the fellside and under a bridge, but the road was totally flooded and I could not get any further. Thankfully a neighbour phoned later to tell me that he could see that our sheep at Low Park Farm were safe.

Antony arrived back with the pump, and we managed

to pump the water out of the garden, and prevent it from entering into the house. According to an account given by James Day (*Tales of Tebay* by Heather Ballantyne, Orton and Tebay History Society, 2010) they were not so lucky on 8 August 1855:

> It was so dark that candles had to be lit in the inn during dinnertime. At the same time the sike at the back door could not contain the immense volume of water from the west side of the valley and for three hours it forced its way through the kitchen, along the passage and out the front door. The cellar at Low Borrowbridge had to be bailed out several times during the storm.

We had now lived here for six months, and in that time we had experienced the worst snowstorm in living memory, the driest and hottest summer on record, and now probably the most torrential rain since 1855. A neighbour who has lived in the valley all his life had never seen the garden flooded like that since the 1940s. I do sometimes wonder if I attract extreme weather events. I do seem to experience a lot of them.

After the storm we continued getting ready for winter. The concrete arrived and was shaped with wooden shuttering to make two platforms in front of the cow barriers, so that they could eat silage directly from it. Our 'wooding' at Low Park Farm also continued apace, as the woodland fringes were coppiced and trailer load after trailer load of wood was brought back up the farmyard. It would need to be left for at least a year to dry out and 'season', and then the idea was that Fergus would split it and sell it to guests at the holiday cottages.

We had one final sheep fair to attend, the end of season

Lakeland Fair, where we would hopefully be able to go and buy the rest of the sheep that we needed. We were sitting in the kitchen the day before the sale looking at the catalogue when we got a call from someone who was having to sell her flock. This was a very respected flock of Rough Fell sheep, so Hector went straight over after work and arranged to buy all of the remaining sheep that he needed. He would collect them the following morning.

The Land Rover had been struggling to start on the colder mornings, so Antony went and got a new battery and fitted it ready for the winter. Unfortunately this somehow triggered the immobiliser to be stuck on, what a good job we had not needed to go to the Lakeland Fair after all. As it was, Hector could go and collect his new sheep in the tractor and trailer. He would have been so disappointed not to get to the sale if he still needed sheep.

The Land Rover was left stuck in the middle of the farmyard, a problem for another day. How often is our source of frustration on the farm to do with this Land Rover? I do wish that our red one had not been stolen as it was much more reliable.

After the new sheep arrived on the back of the tractor Hector and I bolused them and treated them for any worm or fluke infestation, then walked them down to Low Park Farm. We picked up seven stragglers along the way that had escaped from the field that they were meant to be in. We also passed the sheep that had been attacked by the dog, happily living within sight of the other sheep but still very withdrawn and weak. I called to her but she did not want to walk down to Low Park with us, so I left her there.

You may be surprised that a sheep can make a decision

like this, but in my experience sheep are not only very sociable animals living in family groups, they are also capable of making some decisions for themselves. Some sheep like to live in large groups, and some, particularly Herdwicks, like space and time to themselves. They all have their own personalities and the older sheep will know their own limits. Like teenagers, younger sheep often need a lot of guidance about what they should be doing, and where they should be. They have to learn what behaviour is appropriate. Jumping over walls and generally marauding around the countryside is not appropriate, and in time they will learn this by being taken back to where they should be. It can be an exasperating process, and of course there will always be those who do not want to conform.

So far the autumn/winter had only claimed one casualty, one of the gimmer lambs that was adopted on to the Herdwick that lost her lamb. It may have been that this lamb did not have enough colostrum at birth so she did not have the strength to grow and survive her first winter. Thankfully this was our only casualty so far, we did have one of the new tups with a sore foot, and one of the Ouessants with a constant 'runny bum', but these problems were to be expected and had to be dealt with as a matter of course.

The fields had grown grass after the second cut of silage, ready to 'flush' the sheep before tupping. This is when the female sheep are put onto lovely rich grass in the hope that they will conceive twins. Their bodies produce more eggs when they are on rich grass, in the assumption that they will have a plentiful supply of grass during their pregnancy to help their twins grow. This is an old shepherding technique to produce more lambs.

We had the sheep, the grass, the winter feed and the tups standing ready and waiting for action. In my mind's eye I could imagine all the lambs in the spring. Being able to look forward is a crucial skill for a shepherd. Your mind must be several steps ahead, confidently anticipating a good crop of lambs, otherwise it can be very difficult to endure the winter without a positive frame of mind and outlook.

Undoubtedly there would be difficulties this winter. There would be tears of frustration and times of quiet disappointment, but we had done our best to prepare our farm and ourselves for winter. We were ready for whatever winter was about to throw at us, we just needed to find a way to sort out the electrics on the Land Rover and get the immobiliser off. There was always something.

With the help of a friend messaging me on Twitter we managed to solve the electrical problem. We would never have been able to work it out on our own. The problem was that the wire connecting the door light had snapped. This light connection is crucial to the immobiliser mechanism. We managed to pull the wire out from the door casing and reconnect it. We could see it was working because the door light was going on and off. Thankfully we then managed to start the engine. What a varied skill set you have to have to be a hill farmer. There was always something new to learn, and life was certainly not dull.

We knew that the last weekend of October was going to be busy. Hector had hired a digger to get on with some drainage work, and he left at 5.30am on Saturday morning to go and pick it up. He had to wake the owner up, and he was back with the digger before breakfast raring to get going.

Young sheep.

My parents had come over early as Dad was going to help Hector with the drainage work, and after breakfast Dad and Hector set off in the tractor towing the digger on a trailer down to Low Park Farm and I made my way upstairs to get dressed. I was at the top of the stairs when the phone rang, and Mum shouted up that I had to get dressed very quickly and out into the yard.

I didn't bother getting dressed, put my coat and hat on over my pyjamas and ran outside. The cows had got out overnight and were heading up the road towards Mum and I. Hector had discovered them eating through the plastic on his stack of silage bales, and instantly the decision was made that they were now coming in for the winter. The cows ran up the lane towards me, and then straight into a field with an open gate and headed off towards the river. I asked Mum to go inside and ask Antony to come out and help. Antony had been working in Paris for the first half of the week, and then at St Andrews University on Thursday and Friday. He had got in very late on Friday night, and was not amused to be asked to come out in his short pyjamas and slippers to help with the cows, especially when his legs got nettled.

We managed to get them out onto the lane again, but they turned quickly and started running away from the farm. Hector sped through fields on his quad, and overtook them, jumped off the quad and over the wall, and managed to send them in the right direction. This time they went straight into the yard, and into the cow building. Thank goodness.

Hector and Dad then headed off to do their digging job, and I went back inside to get into some outdoor clothes. The jobs needed to be completed quickly today, and hot soup delivered on the quad down to Low Park Farm for the workers, before I set off to the Luke Fair at Kirkby Stephen auction with Mum. I warned her that it would go on for hours, and be freezing cold in the auction ring. I was right about one of those things.

The Luke Fair is a tradition in Kirkby Stephen, and the pens of animals used to fill the streets on the last Saturday in October, although nowadays it is held in the indoor auction. Before the auction starts a town crier reads the King James I charter. This dates back to 1605, and has to be read aloud once a year by a crier standing on the charter stone in the town for the market charter to be renewed. This allows the town to hold a weekly market as well as the live-stock auctions. The original charter was given to the town by Edward III in 1353, and I suppose over the last 500 years a lot of my ancestors must have bought and sold live-stock at the Luke Fair.

When we arrived there was nowhere accessible to park, and I looked about for someone to help reverse the Land Rover into the one remaining tight space. I had to knock on the window of a pick up and ask a man who was eating his sandwiches in the car park, but he gladly helped.

Once inside it became clear that the tup sale was not going to start at 2.30pm as advertised, as the breeding ewe sale was not yet half way through at 2pm. Mum and I had a look at the tups for sale. One of Hector's Texel tups was limping, and he wanted a cheap white Texel tup to 'jack up' (follow on) after the good tups: budget £200. We made some annotations in our programme, and I picked out six Texels that I liked with small heads for easy lambing. There were also two Blue Texels, and I rang Hector to see if it would be ok to buy one of those. The reply was "yes, but you'll never afford it."

After we had had a cup of tea in the café there were still quite a few gimmer lambs to be sold, so I said to Mum that we may as well go and watch the sale. We took our seats, right under a heater. It was absolutely boiling. My cheeks were bright red, and I felt as if I was going to go to sleep it was so hot. What kept me awake, however, were the prices. The first pen of Swaledale lambs sold for £22 after we sat down, and then several pens unsold. One big group of 30 lambs sold for £12 each, making them the cheapest sheep I think I have ever seen sell at auction. I couldn't fit them in my small trailer, so there was no point me buying them.

The next pen to come in had fewer in number, and a female seller wearing a sling with a sleeping baby in. The bidding reached £6. I could not let them go at that, and so bid £8 each. I did not expect to buy them at that, but then the hammer came down and I had bought them. Good, solid little Swaledale lambs for £8. The seller then gave me £2 per lamb back in luck money, making them £6 each. It had been on the BBC news earlier in the week how the prices were down at Kirkby Stephen auction, but I had never expected them to be this low.

Next came the tups. First of all the Swaledale tups, with registered pedigree tups making £40, then the Bluefaced Leicesters to cross with Swaledale ewes to make mules. Then finally the 'continental tups'. The first one that I had marked as a possible purchase made about £300, and the next £550 – out of my price range. The next two that I had picked both came into the ring looking like they were in the mood for a fight, charging at their current owner and knocking off a gate at the side of the ring. A bit of feistiness in a tup is very desirable, but I did not fancy getting these tups into my trailer never mind unloading them at home.

Next came a run of tups from a very high hill farm. The lady said that she had used all the tups twice on 50 sheep per year. They were distinctly average looking tups; they had not been washed for the sale, and were making about £200 each. This was my budget, and they looked ok with small heads, so I bid on one and was surprised to get him for £60. As a follow up tup he would do nicely, and if Hector did not like him it was not the end of the world at £60.

Mum started talking to me because she had seen my uncle on the other side of the ring and was wondering if she should go and talk to him, but I had to concentrate now because the blue Texels were coming into the ring. I don't know why I liked these over the white ones, but they were small and very chunky and I was going to have a go at buying one. Having already spent £84 of my £200, my budget was £116.

Ordinarily, I don't think that there was any way in which I would have been able to buy a quality Blue Texel tup for £200, never mind £116, but these were strange times. The weather meant that people were short on fodder for the winter; people were short on money as everyone had sustained losses in the snow in March and subsequent bad lambing, and the threat of Brexit was looming.

These tups would produce lambs that would in theory be born after the UK exited the EU, and there was the threat of leaving without a trade deal that could really harm lamb prices, particularly of hill born lambs with smaller carcases. All of these factors added up to a massive amount of uncertainty in farming, and I bought the blue Texel tup for £80. There was now just the question of how to reverse the Land Rover into the very tight loading bay and get the sheep home.

Buying of stock for the new farm was now almost complete. I managed to get a further three Shetlands from the same breeder to put to the Ryeland tup, and then had the good fortune to contact the breeder of Millican Dalton the Ouessant tup to ask if they had any females for sale. The breeder was planning on emigrating to New Zealand, and sold me his remaining ten Ouessant ewes.

So, to go to the tups in November we had:

          52 Herdwick
          135 Rough Fell
          37 Welsh Hill Speckle Faced
          13 Shetland/Ryeland
          20 Ouessant
          17 Welsh Mountain
          9 Swaledale/Welsh Mountain
Total 283 ewes, and:
          6 Texel
          1 Rough Fell
          1 Ryeland
          2 Welsh Hill Speckle Faced
          3 Ouessant   a total of 13 tups.

We had 40 store lambs still to fatten or sell, and 34 replacement gimmer lambs for the main flock and twelve Ouessant replacements. Fifty Rough Fells and 37 Welsh Speckles would be bred pure to provide replacements for the future. The Ouessants would be bred pure, and the Shetland/Ryelands to the Ryeland tup for fibre production. The rest of the ewes would go to the Texel.

All that remained now was to gather in all the sheep and split them into the correct groups for flushing and tupping. That was a job for the 1st of November, ten days before the tups went in with the ewes, and the start of the new farming year.

November

Today I won't think of any sad things,
Will not think of torture or the rape of nature,
Just today, I won't touch those sickening papers
Will just let myself get swept away by this beautiful day
James *What For?* (1988)

The first of November is traditionally the start of the fell farming year, and we look towards spring and lambing with optimism as we sort our ewes into the correct groups for tupping. It is not a day to dwell on the possibility of a bad winter, a shortage of fodder, or even the threat of exiting the EU without a trade deal and the collapse of the UK lamb market. The first of November is all about looking forward with hope to the new farming year.

The ewes are sorted into groups for the tups, and are moved onto good lush grass that has been free of livestock since the second cut of silage. They then rest there for ten days before the tups are released. The purpose of this 'flushing' is to get the ewes to release more eggs and therefore conceive more lambs. It is a bit like tricking the ewe's body that she will be on very good grass all winter, so she will be fine to conceive a lot of lambs, as she will have all the nutrition that she needs.

We had wondered about not flushing the Herdwicks, but in the end all the ewes were put onto good grass. Our tupping groups were:

- 52 Herdwicks to go to a Texel tup
- 50 Older Rough Fell to go to a Rough Fell tup
- 37 Welsh Hill Speckle Faced sheep to a Welsh tup
- 13 Ryeland/Shetland to a Ryeland tup
- Ouessants not related to Millican Dalton with him
- Ouessants related to Millican Dalton with new tup
- All remaining sheep to two Texel tups.

They would remain in their groups with their tups for seventeen days (one cycle) and then the tups would be swapped around. Hopefully most of them would conceive in the first seventeen days to make lambing easier.

The tups wear harnesses with 'crayons' and mark the ewes when they mate with them. This is so that we can get an idea of when they will lamb, and also if we are getting any 'returns' where a tup revisits a ewe, in which case there might be a problem with tup fertility.

Our day of gathering and sorting the ewes started after the school run, when we brought half of the ewes back to the temporary pens at the bottom of the big meadow at Low Borrowbridge. We had positioned these next to the gate to the big meadow, so that we could put the younger Rough Fells through a gate and into the meadow, and send the older sheep back down the track. They would then be brought back along the track and into their field. The Herdwicks were going into Salters meadow on the other side of the road, and the older sheep back down towards Low Park. The Shetland/Ryeland sheep were put into the quad bike trailer and driven to their field.

It took us until lunchtime to sort through these 175

sheep, and then after lunch we drove down to Low Park Farm to gather the Herdwicks and the rest of the sheep. They had a long walk back to Low Borrowbridge, and the Herdwicks definitely go slower on a gather than the other sheep. This could be because they have always been gathered on foot on the fells, and the other sheep are used to being gathered by quad bike.

We managed to sort these sheep without major incident, and the Welsh sheep were left in the pens while we walked the best Rough Fell sheep to a meadow about a mile away. On the way back we saw that one of the Ouessant tups had escaped, and so we brought all the tups back to wait inside a building for ten days. For all the tups to get loose now and randomly tup the ewes they liked would be catastrophic.

After we walked the tups back to the farmyard we set off back for the Welsh sheep and walked them home into a field near the house. It was beginning to get dark now, and we were just about to congratulate ourselves on a job well done, when we saw five Shetland/Ryeland sheep jumping over a wall and into the wrong group of sheep. That would have to be a problem for another day. We had been on our feet for seven hours walking to and fro, and were ready for a hot bath and a cup of tea. Not even jumping sheep would spoil our optimism about tupping. It was not a day for stress and worry; it was a day to look forward with hope.

Meanwhile the men working on the walls for Network Rail were not making as much progress as they had hoped. This was excellent news for us, as they needed to extend their access requirements by another three weeks, which meant access payments for another three weeks. The flood alleviation works had finished and the bare ground left where the trees had stood was sprayed with a sticky mixture of wildflower seed that clung to the riverbank.

The fishing season was now over, no fishermen were allowed to fish in the Lune after the 31 October, to allow the fish to replenish sustainably. I noticed large numbers of chaffinches around the farm. I had started to feed a small amount of hay to each group of young sheep each day, just in case it snowed, as they would need to know about hay then. The seeds fell from the hayracks while the sheep ate, and the chaffinches hopped about under the hayracks eating seeds. The hens also liked to be in on the action whenever food was involved, and so a curious mixture of hens, chaffinches and sheep ate together.

On the 4 November the first tups went in amongst the ewes. The Ouessants were sorted into two groups, those related to Millican Dalton and those not, and were put in two separate fields, one group with Millican Dalton and one with one of the new tups. At the same time the very late born lambs were weaned and given their second inoculation. Never before had we weaned lambs and put the tup in on the same day, but that is an illustration of the extraordinary year we were having weather-wise.

Millican Dalton set off across the field like a rocket to find his ewes, whereas the new tup sauntered about looking pretty and trying to tempt the ewes to go over to him. They were of very different temperaments. Soon they were both surrounded by curious ewes.

That afternoon I left the farm to go to Walna Scar shepherds' meet. This is a long established Herdwick and Swaledale shepherds meet up, after the meet there was to

Feeding time.

be singing in the local pub, the sixteenth century Black-smiths Arms at Broughton Mills. I was not going to enjoy myself, however, I was going to interview two Herdwick farmers who had recently given up their farm tenancy in Tilberthwaite and handed the farm back to the National Trust to re let, despite being passionate 'Herdwick people'.

They felt that they had to give up their farm because of the pressures all around them with people on 'adventurous' activities – 4 x 4 driving adventures, motorbikes, mountain bikes, etc. They have experienced that the type of visitor coming to the Lake District has changed in recent years, rather than those who ramble around the lanes and on the fells, happy to observe the environment and stand aside whilst a farmer passes by with his sheep, the modern visitor races along on a mountain bike trying to get a good time for a segment on an app, and rides straight through the flock without regard for shepherd or sheep.

There is a general feeling that popular areas are becoming not only 'honeypots' but also pressure cookers. Something has to give, and in this case it has been their decision to leave the farm. What sort of visitor we want to encourage to the Lake District, and how these visitors can co-exist alongside traditional farming practices, should surely be considered carefully in the future. Farmers working in Cumbria often spend 365 days a year on their farm, within a couple of miles of their home. Is it appropriate for other businesses to also use that space for activities that do not fit well with farming? The debate will no doubt continue, as they leave their farm to a somewhat uncertain future.

I was working with a photographer, Bill Robertson, who had photographed the farmers preparing their sheep for the last show before leaving their farm, selling their sheep at auction and showing their sheep before they left the farm. Both Bill and I felt it was important to let the pictures tell the story so that people could realise the pressures that fell farmers are under.

Meanwhile as we approached the time for the rest of the tups to be 'loosed' we still were not happy with the condition of some of the Herdwicks. Despite grazing on very good grass they were still looking very thin. They had not taken very well to the lush grass after living at a much higher altitude, and had an inclination to browse around the edges of the fields rather than eating the middles. It could have been just this that was keeping them thin, or it could have been fluke. We decided to dose them again with a different flukicide, and got them in on the 7 November and dosed them.

We needed to make sure that the gimmer lambs, the flock replacements, would know to eat hay if it snowed, and so we put them inside one of the barns for three days with only hay and water. They all started eating hay, and were now 'haybitten' ready for the winter.

Most hill farms send their gimmer lambs away for 'wintering' for the first winter, to kinder climes somewhere. We had decided to keep ours at home, down at Low Park Farm, so we loaded them into the trailer and delivered them down the valley. They seemed very happy grazing around the deserted farmhouse, but so they should on about two acres per sheep!

I was also busy during November planting out haymeadow plants that I had grown earlier in the year at local primary schools as part of a project for Cumbria Wildlife Trust. Hopefully they would establish themselves over the winter and grow the following spring so that the children in the schools could learn to identify them.

The night before the majority of the tups were due to go in with the ewes, the ewes were getting pretty giddy. They kept running about. Antony came in from fell running on the Howgills and told me that there were about 20 shearlings out. It was not a surprise. I went out on the quad to get them back into the meadow, and then thought I had better have a ride along to the common to check that no more ewes were heading for the open fell.

It's a funny thing but the motorway and the railway are both much more noticeable at night. I got along to the cattle grid, no more ewes to be found, and then sat looking across the valley. I was the only human moving about in the Lune Gorge. All was silent in the other four houses in the valley, people were probably tucked up inside as it was a stormy night. I had my little light on the quad, and my two little lights in the valley looked dwarfed by hundreds of passing trucks on the motorway with their side lights on, and a passing Virgin Express train. It was a very strange feeling to be living in such a lonely, isolated spot without another human in the landscape, but with thousands of unconnected humans whizzing through the farm.

I was reminded of an old film that was made about the building of the motorway through the gorge which kept proudly proclaiming 'Progress is coming to the Lune Valley', at which point I kept thinking 'yes, whether it wants it or not.' Very little has actually changed in the valley. Yes, I am driving a quad bike, but I am still a shepherdess looking for lost sheep, and how many who have come before me in the valley will have been out in the dark doing just the same? I felt more connected to the shepherds of the past than to the motorway traffic.

On the 10 November the remainder of the tups had their harnesses and crayons put on and went in with the ewes. The farming year was starting again. We had to keep on keeping on, despite the uncertainty of Brexit without a trade deal and possible taxes on red meat which were the latest anti-farming discussion points in the media. Sheep farming in the Lune Gorge had been a continuous cycle for a thousand years, and it was our job to keep the valley's grass populated by sheep turning it into protein for food. As another storm rolled along the valley bringing high winds and torrential rain, our task was to hold tight and weather any storms that the winter could throw at us – political or meteorological.

Winter Arrives

By mid-November it was starting to feel very wintery. Some of the animals were now inside until warmer weather, and the routine of winter-feeding had begun. During summer I sometimes long for the routine of winter-feeding, but once you start feeding it feels as if you are there for the duration. No days off the farm until spring.

The working day started with 'doing up' in the barns. The cows were inside and may have needed a fresh bale of silage. Every third day they were mucked out with the tractor. The cows went through into a pen in the sheep shed while the tractor drove up and down 'scraping out' the muck, then replenished the straw in the area that does not have cubicles. The side with cubicles did not need straw, as the animals lie in such a way in the cubicle that they keep it clean. All the cows had an area at least 5m by 25m to walk about in, with drinking troughs at the side, plus the cubicles or sleeping area in a raised up area to lie on. They could look out into the yard and watch what was going on. They often came over to have a look and a head scratch. They were very happy indoors and sometimes would have a wander into the yard and back again. Given a choice they were soon back inside.

In the 'lean to' were the tups whose turn it was to wait to meet the ewes. They needed fresh hay and water every morning, and some of them liked a head scratch too. In the

large sheep shed were the commercial lambs being fattened. They lived in a large area, twenty metres square and
needed to be fed with hay and bedded down with straw
each morning. Their water troughs did not refill and needed
to be manually filled.

Also in the sheep shed were the Ouessant hoggs. They
were too young to encounter a tup and must be kept safely
out of the way of all the tups. If they got pregnant as a hogg
the pregnancy or the birth could kill them.

Once the yard was 'fed up' there were animals outside
to check. First I checked all the rare breeds with their tups,
and Ruby came with me on foot to help out and get some
exercise. We carried hay, made into small bales deliberately
for me to carry like this, out to the sheep and checked that
the tups were alright. We might also need to fill up the
water troughs from the river with buckets, although it usually rained enough to do this.

Ruby then went back into the house and I fed the farm
cats, and let the 20 free-range hens out and fed them. Some
wily hens ran as fast as their frilly knickered legs would
carry them over to the sheep shed to see what was going
on over there. They liked to kick the fresh straw about (and
lay eggs in it which was not ideal).

There were then five fields of ewes and tups to check.
We were checking that all the tups looked well and that
their crayons were still in the correct position, and that all
the ewes looked well. We had put out high energy lick
buckets and these needed to be moved every day to avoid
the area around the bucket from getting muddy. The ewes
did not need to be fed yet as they still had sufficient grass.

The gimmer hoggs, down at Low Park Farm also

needed to be checked, just to make sure that none of them were stuck in brambles or had their head stuck in a fence. This took almost an hour on the quad, due to the distance involved in getting there. Of course this used petrol, and contributed to our carbon usage on the farm. I had tried to do a carbon calculation; using material provided for farmers, and it came out that the farm absorbs 24.8 tonnes of carbon per year. It was only a quick calculation, and Antony told me that I should have also included the carbon needed to erect the buildings in 1969, so at some point I will need to do a more accurate calculation.

In November red meat was again in the news, with a suggested tax on red meat. There was also an article in a daily newspaper that said that if you turned to a vegan diet you would save 0.84 tonnes of carbon per person per year. When our farm was producing meat and absorbing carbon, this was clearly not always true. I thought that I would have to do more research into the farm's carbon footprint, and then write an article about this, challenging the notion that becoming a vegan is always positive for the environment. Processed meat is a very different product to the meat that we produce and sell directly to the public.

Once all the animals had been checked it was usually lunchtime, and then after lunch the eight dogs all needed exercising. We did not use them around sheep at tupping time, as the sheep needed to be kept calm and relatively still as they became pregnant. Thankfully since the tups went in they seemed to have calmed down.

After the dogs there was then usually about two hours of daylight left for 'winter jobs'. Winter is a good time to do maintenance jobs like walling, hedging and fencing.

Hedging cannot be done at any other time due to nesting birds. We hoped to lay our hedges traditionally this winter.

There was a vast amount of wood to collect and bring back to the farm. This was because we had been trimming off branches in a lot of the woodland strips. This will allow light to come into the woodland areas, and allow more flowers to grow, and will also make it easier to fence off our riparian strips along the River Lune.

Every time someone had a spare hour, they trundled off down to Low Park in either the tractor or quad with a trailer to bring wood back. The wood was then piled into the old silage pit and cut up with a chainsaw, split with a log splitter and piled up to dry and be used as firewood. Hector and I went down one wet afternoon on the quad, to load the little trailer up with some branches. The branches were at the bottom of the allotment, in the culvert where I had discovered the Himalayan balsam, so quite a remote spot.

We loaded the branches and then set off back again, but no sooner had we set off than the trailer and quad sunk into some peat. I got off the quad, and looked for a minute at the depth of the squelchy peat, thinking about our carbon absorption on the farm, before Hector shouted and woke me from my daydream. The quad and trailer were sinking fast, the tow bar was now not visible where the trailer joined onto the quad, and all four wheels were nearly submerged.

Hector told me getting bogged at the farm where he worked higher up the fell was 'a daily occurrence', and I needed to sit on the front rack of the quad. Every time he attempted to drive out the quad was getting deeper and deeper into its hole. "Quick, unload the wood," shouted

Hector, so we quickly unloaded all the wood that we had just carefully stacked into there.

"You sit on the rack and lean back and do the accelerator, and I'll push the trailer," but the quad kept getting deeper and deeper into the hole. I began to worry that it would be completely submerged.

About two miles away on the fell I could see a tractor going along. I asked "Should I run over and ask him to come through the river and pull us out?"

"Oh yeahm" said Hector, "there's no time mother."

We both went to the back of quad and looked at the situation, and then Hector plunged his arms into the mud and tried to bring the tow bar to the surface. I tried to lift the trailer up at the same time. We both used all our strength,

The quad on safe terrain.

and then there was some movement. Miraculously the wheels of the trailer began to come up slightly.

"Push them to the side," shouted Hector, and soon one wheel was out and on a tussock of grass. I held onto the trailer while Hector unhooked it, and then with both of us sat on the front rack of the quad we managed to get it to drive out of the hole. Hector quickly drove around by the riverbank and hooked on the trailer, and then we were off.

"Like I said, a daily occurrence" he said. We were both totally covered in mud from head to toe. Mud was matted into my hair. Thank goodness we got the quad out. The wood would have to wait a while until the tractor could get down there to retrieve it.

I related what had happened to a friend and she asked

"When you go out on the quad how confident are you that you are not going to get into a tricky situation?"

I replied, "100% if I'm driving, as I haven't got the courage to go on any routes I don't know really well." This was a good illustration of why I should never go on any unfamiliar routes by myself, as there was absolutely no way that I could have got the quad out on my own.

When we got home I had another situation to deal with as I noticed that one of the Ouessant tups was not in his field. Wall or fence jumpers at this time of year can be very costly, as a rare breed sheep mating with a commercial ewe would cause a loss of income. I had to go and look for him immediately, as there would be an embarrassing situation if he had jumped in with someone else's sheep. Thankfully he was amongst my Welsh sheep, and easily caught. Some days it's just one thing after another, and all you want is a cup of tea by the fire to dry out.

The wind and the rain were blowing down the valley in great swathes as I lead the Ouessant tup back home. I realised that there was not a single leaf left on any tree. It was the 14 November, and winter was upon us.

No sooner was winter upon us than illness struck, both for the sheep and myself. One of the shearlings suddenly collapsed and subsequently died. This was disappointing, but we counted our blessings that it was only one sheep. We thought that it had listeria, and in that situation once the sheep has collapsed there is very little that can be done for her other than make her comfortable on some straw in the barn.

I managed to somehow get flu, and was a shivery, sneezy shadow of my former self. Antony was working in London, and Hector at another farm for the rest of the week, so there was nothing for it but to get wrapped up warm, full of Lemsip and attempt to carry on as usual and get all the jobs done. It was very difficult to go back outside after I had huddled near the Rayburn warming by the fire at lunchtime, but there was no choice.

When it was a cold day the engineering workers sent by Network Rail would spend all the working day sat in their welfare cabin on the farm, while I whizzed by on the quad sneezing with two hats and two scarves on. They must have thought I was crazy to be outside in that weather with a cold, but there really was no option. After all the animals were checked and the dogs walked I collapsed into bed before my alarm went off to tell me to go on the school run. I'm sure such times are character building.

The days were getting shorter and there was a general area of impending doom as dark clouds hung above the valley for days. One evening we went out in the car up out of the Lune Gorge as the sun was setting and the sky was pinky red on the horizon. The gorge is so steep sided that when we are on the farm we cannot see the sun setting, and I know it sounds stupid but I had actually forgotten that sunsets could be so beautiful after living at the bottom of the gorge for seven months. I wonder what the Roman soldiers made of living at Low Borrowbridge after coming from Italy. At least they had central heating. I wonder if they were like our engineers and did not venture out on cold days. Roman soldiers, navvies, motorway construction workers and modern engineers, all sent to work in the Lune Gorge in all seasons. My challenge now was to keep on working despite feeling lousy, and hope the forecast snow did not come while I was ill.

Flu and Breakdowns

The flu lingered on for two weeks, during which I seemed to have every kind of mechanical breakdown known to man, in addition to my physical breakdown. Two days running I got a puncture on the quad that had to be repaired. Ponies broke down fences and were running about alongside the Lune, lambs broke out of the building and were running about in the farmyard. It was as though everything and everyone was deliberately making as much work as possible for one poorly human.

The worst thing that happened was another sudden death. This time it was my Blue Texel tup that I bought at the Luke Fair in Kirkby Stephen in October. For no apparent reason he just dropped down dead before he had even had chance to meet the ewes. I'm not really a fan of Texel sheep, but I did like this one, as he was so friendly. I called him Benny and he would come over for a scratch. What a short life.

My only conclusion was that he had possibly been 'forced' too much before the sale – fattened on commercial foods and encouraged to grow bigger than he would have naturally, but that is just a guess. Once something is dead it is dead, there is no going back. If it is an isolated death it is probably too time consuming and costly to investigate, and we must just chalk it up to experience. If a pattern of illness or death establishes itself it must be investigated to prevent other animals from getting ill.

With a flat tyre on the quad and a broken down Land Rover it was up to me to move the body for the fallen stock collection. He seemed to weigh an absolute ton. I had to tie bailer twine around his legs and haul him across the yard. There was no way I could lift him into the wheelbarrow. He made a very sorry sight lying upside down waiting for the collection.

Thankfully when the RAC arrived to look at the Land Rover the following morning they could start it straight away. The emergency fuel cut off had come on for some reason, and it was simple task to switch it back on. Meanwhile, the quad that had been at the agricultural engineers since August was apparently fixed, and they promised to return it soon. The repairs had cost around £900, and as it was under warranty they asked us to pay £200 towards that, which seemed fair enough. Anything to avoid paying £900!

It was not all good news, however. The Land Rover doors had been recently replaced at a cost of £1,000, and when Storm Diana blew down the valley on 28 November it blew off one of the doors as Hector opened it. It also blew his caravan over and across a field. The weather was totally wild; rain was blowing in around the south facing windows in the house where it had never done before. Hector was helping a friend pack his possessions into a trailer ready to move house the following day. His friend was moving from Cumbria to Perthshire in Scotland, and Hector had volunteered to drive his tractor the 200 miles there for him.

They decided to make it into a charity sponsored tractor run for the Royal Agricultural Benevolent Institution. It was a laudable thing to do, but the night before the tractor run was due to set off at 4am I was hoping that they would change the date and do it when the weather wasn't so stormy. They had already raised around £350 before they set off, by asking for sponsorship at the Rough Fell Sheep Breeders annual general meeting.

Meanwhile I was continuing to look after the sheep with the flu. Grass was becoming a scarce commodity and all the sheep needed moving around. This involved taking groups of sheep from one field to another along the length of the farm. Going there was into the wind, and it was hard to stand up at times. Any windier and I would have had to abandoned moving them. Sometimes it is just safer to leave animals where they are rather than try to make them move about in the wind. When I got to the furthest point of the farm, about three and a half miles form home, I was just abut to turn back when I saw a figure in orange walking across the fields to meet me.

It was an engineer from Network Rail, he had called at the house to see me but no one was in, so he had set off initially in his car and then on foot to find me. He was asking permission to do more work on the farm boundaries. He said, "I bet you think I'm a real pain wanting to do work again." To which I said, "Not at all, I really need the money!"

I was also told that the work to fence off the dangerous culvert would begin the following Monday, which was music to my ears. The last thing we wanted in storms like this was an animal falling into a culvert full of gushing water. We walked back to his car together, him commenting on his amazement that I was out moving sheep in this weather with a streaming cold, and me commenting on my amazement that he had walked so far to find me after his car could not travel any further on the rough track.

Our cows were happily settled inside eating hay and silage, but the man who had agreed to winter his cows here was proving very elusive. He had agreed a price and said that he would bring them at the beginning of November. At the beginning of November he had messaged to say that the weather was so good he would bring them in two weeks time, but since then no communication at all. We were relying on the income. It was difficult to know what to do. Should we sell the silage instead? We would make less money, but at least we would have some money, or should we hold out for the cows hoping that they were going to come soon?

The decision was made when a neighbour came round asking if we would sell him some of the silage. A price was agreed and the silage sold. We had money in the bank, we had weathered another storm, the tractor run to Perthshire had thankfully been uneventful, and it was almost advent. Things could be worse.

December

After a few murky, misty, damp days at the beginning of December we at last had a beautifully crisp morning. The sky opened up above our heads, and was blue for what felt like the first time in weeks.

Still having quad and Land Rover issues, we set off in the tractor to check all the sheep. I had to stand up in the cab while Hector drove, and every time we went over a bump my head hit the overhead switches and the windscreen wiper came on. Hector would say 'wiper', and I would fumble about, lose my balance and end up knocking it on again.

We drove for about two miles like this, and then decided to walk the last mile and a half. Several more trees next to the river had come down in the recent storms, and we discussed each one, debating whether to remove it for firewood or leave the dead wood there for animal habitats. If we knew that there were a profusion of woodland plants in that area, we would be likely to suggest that the tree was removed for firewood to allow the woodland floor plants to flower. If there were not many plants there, we usually decided to leave the rotting tree trunk, while cutting off the branches and laying them next to the tree. This will allow plants in the surrounding area to flourish, and deadwood is an important animal habitat that also releases nutrients as it slowly decomposes. It also improves the ability of the soil to retain water.

It was quite difficult to remember what plants had been growing where during the spring and summer, but we will improve our knowledge with time and become more skilled at managing the biodiversity on our farm as the years roll on.

All the sheep were looking well in the cold, crisp sunshine, so we were happy to leave them as they were, without moving them or feeding them at the moment. The majority of sheep had been marked as tupped during their first seventeen day cycle with the tup. Out of the 50 Rough Fells put to the Rough Fell tup only one had got pregnant after the initial seventeen days. It was going to be a busy time next spring with a lot of the sheep lambing in the first two weeks of lambing time.

Men sent by Network Rail had arrived to fence off the dangerous culvert at last, and brought with them a gator to drive the length of the land to get them to the culvert and back. It was good to see progress being made.

After one day of sunshine the rain set in again. Great curtains of rain were blowing down the valley without any respite. There was only one thing to do, steel myself and get outside in it checking sheep and walking dogs. The hardest time was going out again in the rain after being by the fire at dinnertime. It helped to have two waterproof coats that could be worn and dried in rotation, and a large collection of hats and gloves.

It's at this time of year when you find out if you really have the temperament for hill farming. Can you stay outside in the rain, usually on your own, during all daylight hours and put up with the wind and the rain being thrown against you all day? Can you accept that winter is like this, and just get on and complete your work in this weather? You have to be somewhat of a realist, accepting the weather for what it is, and somewhat of an optimist, looking forward to spring time and lambing.

Throughout most of December there is no tinsel, tree or fairy lights in the farmhouse, but there are plenty of mince pies and cups of tea. Hot food needs to be eaten three times a day, with another two tea breaks for hot drinks. It's amazing the amount of food that you need to eat during winter to keep you on your feet and operating successfully in bad weather.

The whole family runs on tea. We will have at least five cups a day, at mealtimes and tea breaks, when anyone who is 'on site' will sit at the big table in the kitchen and wait for the tea leaves to brew for a proper cup of tea leaf tea. I cannot imagine winter without tea; I don't know how I would be able to keep going without refuelling regularly on hot drinks.

All the family drink tea, the boys started drinking it warm in their baby bottles from the time when they were toddlers. Drinking tea together allows us to regroup and chivvy each other along. Some days I am on my own with Ruby for my tea breaks, some days the rest of the family are around, or perhaps my parents. Some days Antony's uncle was here measuring up the house for us and producing architectural drawings. Whoever was on site, and whatever they were doing, everybody stopped for tea.

Stopping for tea is one thing, starting again is quite another. You have to be very self-motivated to get yourself back outside, because as a hill farmer nobody else is watching the clock or telling you what to do. You have to have the ability to keep on going, keep on working and get the job done without anybody else working alongside you or telling you what to do. Hector often says to me that I work all day and get nothing done. By this he means that I am busy all day doing routine animal jobs and never get any fencing or farm improvements done. That is true, I like to see that all the animals are checked every day, and all the dogs are walked, and that can take some considerable time. During the middle of winter there is no time to do anything else.

Once it is dark I will go into the house and do my ironing or cleaning before the afternoon school run. It is not the ideal time to do cleaning after 3pm, but that is the way that it has to be in winter because the days are so short for getting animal jobs done. It becomes almost unimaginable that in summer we could be outside in daylight at 10pm, when you cannot see to walk across the farmyard at 4pm in winter.

On the Jeremy Vine Show on BBC Radio 2 there is a regular feature called 'What makes us human'. A guest comes in each week to talk about what makes them human, their work, relationships, etc. What makes me human is the need to look after my animals in all four seasons. There are a huge variety of weather conditions in the year, and throughout them all I must be outside tending to the flock. That is what makes me human. I would hate to live somewhere where there are not pronounced seasons, as the seasons are a huge part of my life, good and bad. We are always very aware of the weather, it is often causing anxiety and lack of sleep, but it makes us in no doubt that we are part of this landscape, we are not casual observers, and we do not control the landscape or the seasons. That is what makes a hill farmer human.

The hill farmer understands in no uncertain terms that they are only human; they are not some sort of deity who controls the land and the landscape. The human must work with the forces of nature, and not fight against them. It is easy to understand this merely by stepping outside the farmhouse door and seeing the scale of the landscape, the hills steeply surrounding the house with their lofty tops more than a thousand feet above our chimney pots. The human feels like a tiny part of the landscape, not the controller of it. I know as well that it is a privilege to be able to step outside the door and stretch my eyes along the Lune Gorge, not all people have the luxury of space and a view.

It may be a long hard slog in December, but it is still an absolute privilege to be here. We work long hours for very little money. We have no heating in the house, apart from coal fires. Going outside and across the farmyard in the dark to get a bucket of coal to fill up the stove so that you can have hot water and a bath sometimes feels like the final straw after a day of pushing yourself to the limit physically and mentally, but in June when the lambs are skipping about in the fields it will all be worthwhile. The promise of spring and lambing will keep us going throughout the wet, wild, dark months.

On some days we will be in absolutely no doubt that we are only human, when we have lost a battle to keep an animal alive, or seen that one has slipped and drowned while getting a drink from the river raging along in spate, but we know that we are human and not superhuman. We accept our limits and know that there is only so much that we can do. With a nod or a shrug we are on to our next job, not looking back, keeping on and doing our best. At the end of the day that is all we can do, and if we have honestly done our best and nature has beaten us on this occasion, so be it. We accept that.

If this year has taught us anything it has taught us that we are only human. I think that it will have given my son a tremendous depth of character and understanding of his place in this landscape. If he is as keen at the end of this year to farm this landscape as he was at the beginning of the year when we bought the farm, then I don't think he will have any problems with motivation throughout his working life. This year has challenged us all physically, emotionally and financially, but we have made it to the end of the year and we are still smiling in the short, dark days of winter.

A journalist from the *Farmers' Guardian* came to interview me about taking on the farm and the first year. She asked how it was working with my son, and when he returned from his other job that evening I asked him what he would have said to her if he were here. He said "We're good pals, and I like work working with you." I'll settle for that.

The Silver Christmas

Work must be done on the farm every day during the year, even Christmas Day, but we must still make time for Christmas and make sure that we have some sparkle in our lives in December. This year was going to be a different Christmas to recent years because my eldest son was going to spend it in Edinburgh not here on the farm, and we also had another event to celebrate.

I was born on 14 December, and often when I was young the school Christmas party would take place on my birthday. This would be an excuse for all the staff to give me 'the bumps' in the middle of the Christmas party, but when your birthday is at Christmas it often just gets subsumed into the general atmosphere of the fortnight before Christmas. I always vowed that if I were to get married I would get married in the summer, so that my wedding anniversary was in the summer months. Of course real life does not always work out like that, and we were married on the 18 December after Antony had finished his final term at university in 1993.

That meant that 25 years later, we were celebrating our Silver Wedding Anniversary in 2018. Oscar was able to come back for the anniversary, so we decided that we would have a 'Silver Christmas' meal this year on the 15 December. We invited both our families and set about making preparations.

We needed to seat twelve people, so decided that we would use the old courtroom that was attached to the house. This had never been decorated or heated since we moved in, and was a cold 1960s space. There wasn't much I could do about the décor now, but I went out to buy some silver decorations. I also bought silver tablecloths, crackers and napkins, etc. I got home and set about decorating the room and setting the table. It didn't look bad, but it was still freezing cold. I suggested that we light the fire, and soon the flames were roaring up the chimney. All seemed to be going well until a bird's nest came down the chimney, followed by all the smoke, and then a large soot fall. All the silver decorations and tablecloths were now covered in a thick layer of soot, as were all the carefully wrapped Christmas presents for our families that I had left at the side of the room. Black smoke filled the house. The doors and windows had to be opened, making the whole house freezing. It was not a good start.

Not to worry, said Hector, he had seen a lovely Christmas tree in one of our woodland strips that he was going to go and bring back for us. I should have questioned the size of the tree when I saw him go off with the chain saw and a large sheep trailer. The tree was quite spectacular, but there was no way it was going to fit in the house. When we had removed a couple of feet of trunk, which went into the Rayburn and burnt with the end sticking out, we tried to get the tree into the house. The end of the tree fell out of the Rayburn onto the kitchen floor, and although I couldn't get into the kitchen as I was on the wrong side of the Christmas tree, I gathered that it had somehow set the lino floor alight.

The tree was then manoeuvred into the sitting room, but only once we had removed most of the furniture from the room, as it filled about half the room. It was then left, abandoned for the rest of the day, as it was too dark to go outside and find stones to prop it up. It was tied to the window frame but leant at an alarming angle right across the room, so that if you entered the room you were met by huge branches coming towards you like tentacles.

The Silver Christmas was certainly shaping up to be a highly individual event, and with snow forecast for the day we began to wonder what else could go wrong. Thankfully two chimney sweeps were able to come and save the day, bringing a huge bird's nest down from the chimney and getting the fire working again. They had also just been to a farmhouse where the owners were removing a large range and replacing it with a wood burner, and it might be possible for us to us to have the range, so perhaps the soot fall was in fact a blessing in disguise.

Work continued as winter tightened its grip on the valley. The tups had now been in with the ewes for 34 days, two reproductive cycles, so in theory they should now all be in lamb. As a finale to tupping time we mixed the groups up a little and moved all the sheep onto fresh grass (although not much of it at this time of year) and put out our final set of tups in addition to our first and second choices. In this final group was my Welsh tup lamb that I had bred this summer, and I was pleased to see him galloping across the field when released and frantically sniffing the ewes to see if they were in season. He had the makings of a really good tup next year.

A couple of ewes were limping, and a couple of

Herdwicks were still looking too thin, but generally our sheep looked better than they ever had before at this time of year. I was proud of the way that the flock were looking. The older Rough Fell ewes in particular were looking as well as any flock of Roughs that I had ever seen. I think that we had bought wisely, from respected breeders, and hopefully they would produce good replacement lambs for our flock for the future.

We were still waiting to hear whether our bid for Countryside Stewardship had been successful. I believe that the decision should have reached us in September so it was now at least two months behind schedule. We were therefore limited in the winter jobs that we could do as we did not know whether we had funding to rebuild walls and create riparian strips. We concentrated on the jobs that we could do that were outside the remit of the schemes, such as putting up a big barn owl box in an old oak tree. Hopefully the owls would use it next year. We had applied for funding for an owl box in our stewardship application, but we had to withdraw that option as were considered to be too near the railway line and the motorway for owls to breed successfully – despite the evidence of our own eyes that they had bred successfully this year.

The Silver Christmas soon arrived, along with Storm Deirdre. Wind was blowing in just the right direction to somehow blow through the kitchen and down the hall. The house was absolutely freezing despite having two sitting room fires and the Rayburn on. Despite this the atmosphere was convivial, and we all enjoyed a lovely three-course meal before our guests were blown away down the valley in their cars.

We celebrated being married for 25 years. A quarter of a century, three children, nine house moves, and here we were embarking on the biggest challenge of our lives. We had a silver wedding cake that I had decorated with pink and white roses, and we had our photograph taken cutting the cake. I was wearing a 1950s style dress with roses on it, and Antony had on his velvet dinner suit. Behind us you can the 1930s fireplace, and the vintage 1960s wallpaper in the courtroom.

It is a curious photograph, it looks like it had been styled to be a vintage event when in fact it is just Antony and I dressing as we like to in our home that needs renovating. People on social media commented that the photo looked like it had been taken decades ago. Sometimes our shepherding lifestyle does seem to fall through time. It is a timeless occupation in a farmyard that has not changed since the last modern buildings were erected in 1969, so the last major renovation/improvement project here was 49 years ago. Thinking about it, it cannot be coincidental that the motorway was opened 50 years ago. The farm has been both inconvenienced by the advent of new transport links coming to the area, and benefitted from them.

I woke during the night after the Silver Christmas meal and looked outside. The world was, appropriately, silver in the moonlight. The promised snow had come. I hardly slept until daylight, but when I got up all the snow had gone. The animals were fine, if a little hungry and windswept. Our guests had all got home safely, secure in the knowledge that our lives are ruled somewhat by the weather here. You are much more aware of the weather here than you would be in a town or city. The weather seems to somehow hold you

in its hand, and have power over you. What you can and cannot do is dictated by the weather – you must wait to see what it's like before you decide upon your jobs for the day. The weather is the biggest challenge encountered in hill farming.

Another challenge is dealing with the Rural Payments Agency. On the day of our silver wedding anniversary I got an email from them telling me that they were unable to pay me my basic payment for 2018 by the end of the year. This is a payment for the whole of 2108, which had to be claimed in May. The reason given was "as your claim contains common land we need to make sure that all the necessary rights information and mapping is complete before we can allocate the eligible area of common land." Bear in mind that they had paid me on this land (at Blawith) in both 2016 and 2017, so surely the calculation cannot be that complicated that it takes over seven months to complete?

The email went on to say that if they have not been able to pay me anything by the end of March 2019, they would hopefully make a bridging payment in April. The email suggested that if I was experiencing 'extreme financial difficulties' I should contact one of 'a number of farming help organisations' – a charity. Yet again, I cannot understand how the government thinks that is acceptable to delay paying people money that they are owed for an indeterminate length of time. Imagine if teachers or nurses were treated like this, and they were told sorry, your overtime is too difficult to calculate, so we will pay you nothing for three months. Farmers have bills and mortgages to pay as well. It is a totally unacceptable situation.

In addition to that 'good' news I also managed to cut

one of my dog's ears on my wedding anniversary. I was trimming the hair around her face when she shook her head and the end of the scissors caught her ear. Although she was fine, and I treated the ear with iodine, I felt terrible. Farming can be a very stressful business at times!

The irony was that I had read the new government regulations for people breeding dogs, and it said that no dogs should have any matted hair on them. My collies generally have a bit of matted hair behind each ear that never gets removed by grooming, so I thought I had better remove that in the interests of animal welfare. Instead of improving animal welfare for that dog I made her situation worse.

Thankfully the following morning the ear was looking a little better. It had not healed but it looked like it would not cause any significant problems. I was so relieved as I had been feeling sick with anxiety all evening. It is a horrible thing to think that you have inflicted pain onto an animal, even if it was unintentional. She certainly showed no sign of being in pain in the morning, and was leaping about like a nutter in her excitement to see me first thing in the morning.

It was not a day for dogs, however, it was a day for working with the gimmer hoggs, the future mothers of the flock. Once all the other animals had been fed and the dogs had been walked Hector and I set off down to Low Park Farm to gather the hoggs. Thankfully it was neither raining nor freezing cold, so ideal weather for working with the sheep. If it had been too wet or too cold we wouldn't have given them their treatments, as it would put too much stress on them in times of testing weather.

We got the hoggs into the pens and set up our footbath.

The first job was to check if any of them needed a pedicure by making them walk about in the pens while we watched them. Thankfully nobody did, so the next thing that we did was run them all through the footbath. This is a preventative treatment to keep their feet in good condition.

After that we got them in groups of about ten into the race. Each sheep was given a dose of fluke/wormer, two new boluses containing minerals to see them through the winter, and an injection to prevent them getting sheep scab or lice. We then checked that they were correctly marked with our flock mark, and sent them back off into the fields around Low Park. They had a lovely big area to spread out into, with about two acres per hogg.

Each treatment that we gave them had to be recorded in our farm medicine book, which I did over lunch. After lunch I set off along the valley delivering Christmas cards, but got a call to come back as our new lamb weigh scales had arrived. We could now weigh the lambs that we were intending to sell for meat. We wanted them to be about 40kg, and disappointingly only about ten of them were between 38 and 40kg. The others would have to stay with us for a while longer, eating hay. With the news that we would not be getting our basic payment scheme money any time soon, it would have been nice to have been able to sell most of the lambs and generate some income that way.

A friend sent me a message to say that she had been to the bank to arrange a loan, as they had also had the same email from the Rural Payments Agency saying that they were not going to be paid. I really cannot understand why the Rural Payments Agency cannot get its act together and administer the payments in December each year when they have had all of our completed claims since May. When you think of the year that farmers have had, with snow and then drought to deal with, the last thing that they need is to also have financial problems. If some bits of land, such as commons, were causing mapping problems, you would think that the rest of the undisputed land could be paid out on while the problem is sorted out.

The country has other priorities, such as Brexit, and the rumour is that a lot of the staff that would normally be working on our claims are making preparations for when/if we leave the EU instead. There was nothing we could do but hold our purse strings tight and hope.

In the Bleak Midwinter

It was very bleak here in midwinter around the time of the winter solstice, make no mistake. Daylight hours were short, it was dark by 3.45pm and gloomy from about 2.30pm. It was relentlessly wet and windy. Sometimes the rain fell as ice, and it stung your face on the quad bike. I had a hat, hood, scarf and 'buff' around my face so that only my eyes were showing, but I was still riding one handed when I could holding one hand above my eyes to keep the ice off.

The quad was in 4-wheel drive, but even so it slid about on the wet and windy tracks. When I was working on my own on days when Hector was at another farm (every day except Monday and Wednesday) I made the decision not to go in for lunch. Instead I just worked through until all the jobs were done, usually about 2.30pm. This was because it was so wet and miserable outside it was demoralising to go into a warm kitchen and then have to go out again. I would rather get all the jobs done, and then go inside in the knowledge that I did not have to put my waterproofs on until tea time.

It was a battle of endurance. The same jobs were stacked up there waiting in a mental list when I woke: silage for cows, hay bales for sheep indoors and around Low Borrowbridge, hens to feed, ponies to check, silage for breeding sheep in the park, bottom meadow, culvert field and

allotment, check the breeding hoggs at Low Park, walk all dogs on four separate walks, clean out kennels and feed dogs. Once the dogs were fed and settling down for their afternoon nap I could go inside and get my lunch.

The promise of spring and lambing time kept me going. In addition to the letter from the Rural Payments Agency about the basic payment being late, I received another letter just before Christmas saying that they had been unable to come to a decision on my Countryside Stewardship application, due to begin on the first day of January 2019. The letter said that the agreement, if agreed, would still start on on the same day, but they could not let me know until 28th February if it was successful. The incompetence of the Rural Payments Agency was making it very difficult to plan financially on the farm, but also to plan the jobs that we hoped to do. We had a list of winter jobs such as walling and hedge laying that we wanted to get on with, but couldn't.

It was an extremely frustrating situation, in the middle of winter without the money we had hoped to get before Christmas, and not being able to plan the work we wanted to do after Christmas. We were not allowed to get on with the work after 1st January and claim later either, the letter said that had to wait until a decision was made. If we did the jobs in January but the agreement wasn't signed until March we would not be paid for them, even though the agreement would be backdated to the beginning of the year. I cannot see the sense in this – as farmers we have limited times of the year when we can work on hedging etc. because of nesting birds.

Not many good things happen at this time of year, apart

from Christmas, but the potential for things to go wrong is huge. The weather may make life difficult, or other problems may arise with the animals. On Christmas Eve I was cleaning out the dog kennels when Hector shouted, "Mum, look at this" and came into the kennels carrying a spade. Lying on the spade was the aborted foetus of a calf, from one of his new cows. When I say 'aborted' this is the general farming term when a pregnancy does not go full term and the foetus is expelled too early. I do not mean that somebody had purposefully aborted it. What an unwelcome Christmas present.

We isolated the cow from the others and now faced an anxious wait to see if any of the other calves were aborted. If they were, it would be probable that the cows had some sort of infection. Hopefully it would be a one off event, perhaps caused by that cow getting knocked by the others or another simple accident. It was Christmas Eve, and I wasn't peering out across the farmyard looking for Father Christmas, I was looking to see that the other cows were all right.

Fergus had got an air rifle for Christmas, and had been allowed to open it early. The purpose of the air rifle was to shoot unwanted crows that were threatening the other birds on the farm. I had recently been to a talk about wading birds and the speaker had cited one of the main reasons that wading birds were failing to get chicks to fledge in our area was the large number of crows that steal the eggs or the chicks. She said that we had created the perfect environment for predators of wading birds.

Fergus had been asking for an air rifle, so as long as he had plenty of target practice to shoot the crows efficiently, it seemed like a good idea. It is one of the aspects of country life that may seem unpalatable to people who do not live in the countryside, but the reality is that crows can be a problem both for wild birds and hens. They quickly learn how to get into a hen house and steal the eggs during the day.

Fergus had been shooting targets all week, and was now keen to shoot a rat that kept coming into the cow barn at night and nibbling into feed bags if there were too many to fit into the feed bin. So what with Fergus hiding with a gun waiting to shoot a rat, and me checking for cows aborting, it was not a very Christmassy scene at Low Borrowbridge. The lights had also broken on the Christmas tree, so the joy that I anticipated would be spreading out of the window and down the lane was not. I had not managed to find the time to make and put up a holly wreath on the door, despite the garden being full of holly. I had had the best of intentions to make the house as jolly as possible, but had not had time to do it.

I had been delayed coming back from my Christmas food shopping by a host of heavenly Herdwicks. I was listening to a radio programme about angels appearing to people at Christmas, and went round a sharp corner to be met not by a band of angels singing, but by a raggle taggle band of Herdwick sheep walking towards me in the dark on an 'A' road. I couldn't leave them wandering, so had to get out of the car in my tweed skirt and encourage them down a lane where there was not as much traffic.

I then drove behind them until they were safely shut into somebody's (very well maintained) garden. I don't think I was the visitor they were hoping would knock on their patio doors on Christmas Eve, and I don't think they were expecting a flock of Herdwicks for Christmas, but in the spirit of Christmas and welcoming the uninvited guest they agreed to keep them in their garden until the owner could be found.

Christmas was coming, and I hoped that we would have time to enjoy our Christmas dinner without incident or disaster.

> *We stood on the hills, Lady,*
> *Our days work done,*
> *Watching the frosted meadows*
> *That winter had won*
>
> *The evening was calm, Lady*
> *The air so still,*
> *Silence more lovely than music*
> *Folded the hill*

Clive Samson, (1910-81)

A neighbour had warned me that the silence on Christmas Eve would be shocking, our ears having become accustomed in winter to the distant hum of the motorway and the whoosh of the freight trains during the night. In summer the leaves on the trees surrounding the traffic infrastructure meant that we did not hear them. In the Lune Gorge, on Christmas Eve, 'silent night' took on a whole new meaning. All was calm, all was bright. For now anyway.

Christmas

On Christmas day we put on our working clothes and made a cup of tea in the kitchen. It was then decided that we would open our presents before we went outside to do our animal jobs. There were not many to open, just those from each other, as my parents were coming over later in the day.

Hector and Fergus had bought me a mug with sheep on, and a book about sheep. Antony pointed to my other present under the tree and said, "open that, but I don't know if you will like it." It was a beautiful print of an otter floating in a river. I loved it as one of the highlights of the year had been seeing the otters playing on the riverbank. We had not seen them for a couple of months now.

As there was no chocolate to eat, but confident that my parents would bring some later, I then went out to begin my animal jobs. I was just loading up my wheelbarrow in the yard when Hector came flying across the big meadow on the quad waving at me shouting, "Mum, Mum". It was with a certain amount of trepidation that I waited for him to turn into the yard, what on earth could have gone wrong now?

"You'll never believe it..." he began "the otters have come back on Christmas morning, and Dad got you that otter print. Come and see." So I walked with Lass and Pegg the Border collies down the lane to Salterwath Bridge, and spent a very happy half hour with both myself and the dogs leaning over the top of the bridge watching the otters. I suppose some people would at this moment be eating their Christmas breakfast in a five star hotel, but I would not trade places with them. What more could you wish for for Christmas than seeing wildlife swimming about happily on your farm?

It was a truly magical moment, the magic of Christmas at Low Borrowbridge. Watching the otters I forgot all about the cow that had aborted, the Rural Payments Agency not having paid us, Brexit and the uncertainty surrounding farming. Here was proof that we were making a difference, doing something worthwhile for the environment around us. As the otters relaxed and splashed about all the anxiety drained from my body. Cares and worries floated off down the River Lune, if only for one day.

We had finished our farming jobs by 1pm, and sat down to a delicious lunch that Fergus and Antony had cooked. We were eating our own roast pork reared here on the farm. After lunch we lit the fire in the sitting room, and although it was difficult to see because of the enormous Christmas tree, Antony had rigged up an old DVD player for us to watch something.

First we watched the Wallace and Grommit animation *A Close Shave* then we watched one of the boys' favourite films, *Whiskey Galore* from 1949. We had seen both of these about 100 times before, but they still made us laugh.

It was then back outside to check the cows and dogs, and fasten the hens in, and before we knew it Christmas Day was over. We were soon tucked up in bed ready for an early start on Boxing Day morning checking sheep. I can see why the country needs a big festival at this time of year to brighten things up, but sometimes it feels like an odd time of year to be celebrating and relaxing as there is so little daylight in which to get the jobs done, and so much to do.

After all the animals were checked on Boxing Day we decided to go and visit Antony's family for the afternoon, and I took the opportunity to read some of Mary Colwell's book *Curlew Moon* about the loss of wading birds in the UK and Ireland. As well as the problem with predation from foxes and crows, Mary states that farming has become so intensified that in many places there is no room for wading birds unless there is associated financial help on the fields they use to nest in, "In other words wildlife has to pay rent on land that is no longer theirs."

This phrase 'paying rent' really troubled me, and I spent the afternoon worrying about farm economics and space for wildlife generally in our farm system in the UK. Will I be able to get environmental schemes approved to pay that rent on our farm, and will the farm itself be able to pay its way without becoming an environmental desert?

I was still thinking about this the next day when, wonder of wonders, a Christmas miracle occurred and the Rural Payments Agency paid me the Basic Payment Scheme money on all our in-bye land that was not difficult to calculate like the fell rights that were still apparently perplexing them. This was a great way to end the year, and Antony got out his computer and put the amount onto his spreadsheet business plan for 2019.

After asking Hector and I a lot of questions he then told us that by the end of next year we would be around £10,000 in debt if we continue as we are doing. One solution would be to increase the number of cows that we have quickly by buying some bucket fed calves in January.

These are calves that have come from a dairy cow crossed with a beef bull. It will be a labour intensive process to raise twelve of these calves, but it looks like it must be done. Antony also spent his Christmas break measuring the house and deciding whether to have oil fired boilers or a biomass boiler, and wondering if we have the potential to produce our own electricity with a small hydro scheme. There is still a lot of work to do.

On New Years Eve we assessed the situation. In order to become profitable, by the end of 2020 we must get two holiday lets here up and running after refurbishing the old coaching inn and court room. In order to let these we will also need to refurbish the sixteenth century farmhouse, removing some milling machinery and piles of old hobnail boots amongst other things, before we renovate the bedrooms.

We will need to get our numbers up to capacity on the farm, and I will have to finish and sell at least 500 copies of a book per year. Then, and only then, will the farm be profitable. At that point I will have spent ten years, from August 2009 to 2019, working with animals without paying myself any wage to establish this farm.

Will it have been worth it? It is now nearly midnight on New Years Eve 2018/19, and I am sitting here on my own in the house, typing away to finish this book. The others have gone to Tebay Social Club. This book, like setting up the farm, has been an absolute labour of love. Given the opportunity to farm, and the opportunity to write this book, there was no other option but to press on ahead. There have been a myriad of choices this year, a thousand decisions about the archaeology, environment and agriculture here, but the question of whether to farm, or whether to write, was never even up for debate.

I guess I was born to be a farmer, and a writer. Thanks to sheer determination and the support of my family, I have become a farmer with a 'proper big farm'. Thanks to you, the reader and to my publisher, I have become a writer. The only thing to do is keep on keeping on, with the writing and the farming. There is much to do; our work is certainly not yet done.

The Farm

Resources at 31st December 2018:

Farmhouse, built partly in sixteenth century and partly in eighteenth entury.

Old bar and tap room (had been used as a Sunday School)

Derelict farmhouse and three derelict barns.

Range of traditional barns including cow shippons with haybarn over, stabling for three horses, hired lads room, hay mew, turnip stores and pigsties.

Milking parlour built in 1947.

Range of modern agricultural buildings including cow shed and lambing shed.

Silage pit and slurry store.

177 Rough Fell ewes and gimmer hoggs

32 Ouessant ewes and gimmer hoggs

52 Herdwick ewes

55 Welsh Hill Speckle Faced ewes and gimmer hoggs

13 Shetland/Ryeland ewes

3 Welsh tups, Ryeland tup and 3 Ouessant tups.

4 Texel tups

44 lambs being fattened

6 Dexter cows

5 Aberdeen Angus cows

2 stabiliser cows

3 Fell ponies

22 Hens

6 Border collies

A terrier and a Lancashire heeler

164 acres grazing and mowing land

16 year old Land Rover

Small sheep trailer

Large livestock trailer

One old International tractor and one old Ford tractor, bale spike and bucket. Massey Ferguson tractor with two bale cuddlers.

One Honda quad bike and trailer.

One woman, two sons (another at university) and a working husband.

Afterword

The aim of this book was to share with you the process of taking on a farm, and all the decisions that we have had to make over the course of the first year in owning it. I have tried to write in more detail in this book, in order that the reader can better understand the daily life of the hill farmer, the decisions that have to be taken and the jobs that have to be done during the year.

It is not an easy thing to buy a farm in a valley that you do not know well, and take over a farm there without making many mistakes. Ideally a transition would occur over several years, such as from father/mother to son/daughter, so that the farm is properly understood. Every farm is like a jigsaw, but the pieces keep changing according to the weather conditions, market conditions and political climate and things no longer fit together easily.

Like the dry stone waller the farmer must become adept at knowing which piece of stone will fit before he goes to the bother of picking it up off the ground. This is my job in the next few years, to be able to anticipate which piece will be required to fit which gap.

Once I've cracked the job, I'll stop writing about it and just enjoy my farming. That may be some years off yet.

Acknowledgements

I do so hate finishing books,
I would like to go on with them for years.

Beatrix Potter

Many thanks again to my publisher and former Westmorland resident Dawn Robertson, without whom this book would never have seen the light of day. Dawn was one of the first people that I told about our plans to buy the farm, and throughout all the difficulties in purchasing it she kept telling me it was meant to be. It is great to know that someone has faith in you!

Thanks to my husband Antony who has worked tirelessly on his own work projects and on our farming business plans to help us achieve our dream of owning a farm, and to my parents for helping us out when we had 'cash flow issues'. Thank you to my sons for their remarkable work ethic, and for putting up with living without carpet, central heating, electric plug sockets in their bedrooms, etc.

Thank you to John, Hilary and Michael Wilson for selling us the farm, helping us settle in, and always providing information and advice when we needed it. Also for providing big tractors to pull out our small tractors when they got stuck in the snow, what a first year at Low Borrowbridge it has been!

Thank you to Bill Robertson, Amy Bateman and

ACKNOWLEDGEMENTS

Suzanne McNally who have provided the photographs in this book. We were determined to get some summer photos this time, and not just dash about when the book was finished in the winter months. Thank you to Bill, Amy and Suzanne for coming over and photographing me in the sunshine.

Thank you to my followers on Twitter (Westmorland-shepherdess@ruslandvalley) and Instagram (Westmorland-shepherdess) for sharing the story with me throughout the year, and the readers of my column in *Cumbria* magazine. Thank you to the local bookshops who have sold my books, and to the local newspapers and magazines that have reviewed them.

Most of all, thank you to you, the reader. I hope that you enjoyed the book. A book is pointless without readers, so thank you for reading my story thus far. You are always in my mind when things are challenging on the farm, I often say, "If nothing else it will make a good story. It might be bad business for farming but it's all good storytelling material."

Believe there is a great power silently working all things for good, behave yourself and never mind the rest.

Beatrix Potter

Spring

Waist deep waves of frozen snow fill the farmyard
Icicles hang from icebound vehicles
The wind picks up the snow and hurls it at the window
I fill the kettle, and gaze outside at the scene.

It is like a computer-generated image of a snowstorm
Sipping my tea, I prepare myself mentally for venturing out
Then hat on, hood up, scarf covering face
Only eyes left exposed to survey the scene

It is a real struggle to walk across the yard
Into the sheep shed where the tiny sheep are safe
Walking down the valley is impossible
The wind picks me up and deposits me in a heap.

I would never have believed the weather
Could be this extreme, this dangerous
I was emotionally unprepared for this
I hope the animals can find the strength to survive it.

Summer

The sun beats down on the dusty meadow
As we rake the scaled out edges into rows of hay
The tractor and baler do laps around the field
Scooping up the rows and making bales of hay.

Later, when the heat is taken out of the sun
I drive the tractor very slowly in first gear
Between the rows of discarded bales
One son throws them on the trailer, one stacks.

Fifty bales will fit onto the teetering trailer
Swaying left then right as we drive slowly to the barn
Bales are thrown down onto the wooden floor
And we stack them floor to ceiling, back to front.

It takes all evening to fill the barn with hay
We all work together until every bale is safely stowed
Then we jump into the river fully clothed
Or into a cold bath to bathe our scratchy skin.

It takes a whole family to make hay this way.
How many families have filled this barn before us?
We are connected to them, united in our purpose
To farm this land and give our family a future.

Autumn

I smell you seeping down the valley
Saturating everything and everyone
The scent comes first, my nose
Realises that the backend is here.

I hear you at night as I lie awake
Rattling around the farmyard
Blowing in and out of the buildings
Cooking up a storm.

I see you as the colours change
The land goes from green to orange
As the bracken dies
Then the trees turn backendish too.

I feel you seeping through my waterproofs
Chilling my bones and freezing my cheeks
You will not leave me alone
Your dampness follows me everywhere.

I taste you in the blackberries in
The hedgerows. There is no going back now.
Summer has gone, leaving the last
Of her sweetness in the fruit.

As soon as I smell you, hear you, taste you
You are gone for another year.
Autumn blows in and blows out
Leaving only the short, hard days of winter.

Winter

I am on my feet, walking, checking sheep
But winter you have nearly finished me off.
Somewhere, from deep within me,
I am finding the strength to carry on.

I do not mean that I am close to death,
Just too close to exhaustion to care
About anything and everything else
Except feeding animals and keeping them safe.

Every day I have a ladder of jobs to climb
Each rung of the ladder is a job completed
A step nearer to sitting by the stove
Drinking tea in a warm, wind free place.

When I am on the quad, head down
Hail stinging my eyeballs and cheeks
I think about that cup of tea
I visualise myself sat by the fire getting warm.

Every day is a step closer to springtime
A day nearer to lambing, to long warm evenings
Scaling out the hay or stacking bales.
I can have that summertime again

But only if I work now, put in the hours
Keep the sheep well through the winter
Get them through to summer without disaster.
Disaster is only a 'named storm' away.

Read More...

books by Andrea Meanwell

A Native Breed, Starting a Lake District Hill Farm,
978-1-910237-24-3

In My Boots, A Year on a Lake District Farm,
978-1-910237-24-3

Lakelanders,
Stories and poems about living in a Lake District valley
978-1-910237-46-5